Through the darkness, I will love myself

Edited by Wallea Eaglehawk,
Nikola Champlin & Padya Paramita

Illustrations by Risa Rinadiputri

MOONRISE
Brisbane, Australia

Through the darkness,

I will love myself

ISBN 978-0-6450486-1-2 (paperback)
ISBN 978-0-6450486-2-9 (eBook)

Cover artwork and internal illustrations by Risa Rinadiputri
Cover design by Paula Pomer and Wallea Eaglehawk
Typesetting by Oda W. Tolsrød

First published in 2021

Moonrise
Brisbane, Australia
www.moonrise.revolutionaries.com.au

Related titles from Revolutionaries

Idol Limerence: The Art of Loving BTS as Phenomena by Wallea Eaglehawk

Related titles from Bulletproof

I Am ARMY: It's Time to Begin edited by Wallea Eaglehawk and Courtney Lazore

Content warning

Please be aware that themes of self-hate, self-harm, violence, attempted suicide, death, trauma, miscarriage and abuse are present throughout this book.

Contents

Contributors

Editors

Wallea Eaglehawk is a social theorist, author of *Idol Limerence: The Art of Loving BTS as Phenomena* and co-editor of *I Am ARMY: It's Time to Begin.* Alongside her creative practice, Wallea is the CEO and Editor-in-Chief of Revolutionaries, and imprints Bulletproof and Moonrise. A scholar of limerence, identity, love and BTS, Wallea identifies as a practicing revolutionary. Find her on Twitter, Instagram and Medium @walleaeaglehawk.

Nikola Champlin received her M.F.A. in Poetry from the Iowa Writers' Workshop and her B.A. from Yale University. She is one half of the Editors-in-Chief at Dream Glow Magazine, a literary journal for BTS ARMY. Her writing focuses on "ecopoetics," which captures the environment in crisis, and she's inspired by BTS' social and political commentary shared through art. Her poetry has appeared in the Denver Quarterly, the Spoon River Poetry Review, the Alexandria Quarterly, and the Cimarron Review, among other publications. You can find her on Twitter @nikola_champlin.

Padya Paramita is a writer and pop culture enthusiast from Dhaka, Bangladesh currently residing in New York City. She is the Co-Editor-in-Chief of Dream Glow Magazine, a literary magazine that strives to legitimise the experiences of writers and artists inspired by the work of BTS. Her work has appeared in them, Color Bloq, Xeno Zine, VRV Blog and more. She is currently an M.F.A. candidate at Columbia University, using creative nonfiction to explore representation of marginalised experiences in pop culture. You can find her on Twitter @padyatheleo.

Contributors

Destiny Harding is a creative based in Canberra, Australia. Outside of her cultural studies she is interested in fandom, BTS, and exploring digital humanities. Find her on Instagram and Twitter @jungefh.

Nabila Tabita (mostly goes by Bita) is a writer, poet, and filmmaker from Jakarta, Indonesia. She enjoys writing about her life or her fictional one, and sometimes even politics. Bita is the Editor of Planet Serotonin and a Youtuber. You can find her on Twitter, Medium, and Youtube @urgeekypoet.

Catherine Truluck is a writer and bookseller from South Carolina, USA. When she is not talking about BTS with her friends or reading YA in her downtime, she tries to write short fiction. Catherine's first full story was her undergraduate creative thesis on healing and interpersonal relationships.

Aparna Zoya is a writer from Kerala, India. She enjoys reading books, writing poetry and short stories when she's not busy fangirling over BTS. You can find her on Instagram @ink_n_words.

Aradhna Juneja or Aru is a student from Delhi, India. She enjoys writing as an escape from everyday life. You can find her on Twitter @knjbibillyhills.

Fatima Ahmad is a writer from Toronto, Canada. Because of her multicultural lifestyle she enjoys exploring social issues which affect marginalised people around the world. She also enjoys writing fiction-especially sci-fi, and poetry. Fatima is a published writer and (future) psychologist. You can find her on Twitter and Instagram @blue_rose4869.

Gabrielle S. Punzalan is a student at Kennesaw State University studying professional writing. She lives with her family in the suburbs of Atlanta. She enjoys writing stories in her free time and dreams of publishing her own book someday. Find her on Instagram @gabby_s.p and Twitter @GabbyS_Pun.

Katie Hulme lives and works in Cleveland, Ohio, USA. She is a wife, mother, and diagnostic medical physicist by day and writer by night. She only recently began to write again, and credits BTS for stimulating the neglected "right half" of her brain in her otherwise "left-brained" world. She is an Editorial Board member for @TheR3Journal and you can find her on Twitter @limeinacoconut7.

Marinelle Uy is a political science student and aspiring writer from the Philippines. Aside from struggling with college papers, she also hopes to complete a fantasy novel one day. *Stolen Hearts, Stolen Souls* is her first published work. You can find her on Facebook as Nelle Uy, and on Twitter as @NelleUy2 and @Nannerlie19.

Lily Low writes on the internet advocating for mental health awareness. With a background in Law, her passion for people and well-being deeply influences her written work. She has been published in *I Am ARMY: It's Time To Begin*, Thought Catalog, saya. magazine, Anak Sastra Literary Magazine, and Overachiever Magazine. Her content can be found on both Twitter and Instagram @lilylowstar.

Alejandra Vera is a Venezuelan aspiring writer currently living in Spain. Through different poetic styles, her main focuses are self-reflection and mental health, using her writing as a method to heal and putting into words hidden thoughts and feelings. You can find her on Twitter, Instagram and Medium @alejandravera16.

Eris Sker is a writer and poet from Koper, Slovenia. She is a student at Columbia University and enjoys writing about mortality, insanity and identity. You can find her on Twitter @erissker.

Ella Fenn is a writer from Sydney, Australia who has been dabbling with fiction of the YA & NA variety for most of her life. When not writing, you can find her working through her endless TBR pile, appreciating all things BTS, in a climbing gym or loitering on her instagram @fennandink.

Fion Tse is a writer from Hong Kong, mostly of prose but also poetry. In her spare time, she likes to read, write, and talk about art, mental health, and education equity. You can find samples of her work at https://fiontse.myportfolio.com/.

Marsha Lenin is a high school student from Melbourne, Australia. She enjoys writing poetry, creating theories from songs, and managing her BTS fan account. You can find her on Instagram @taespompoms.

Preface

Wallea

It was the defiant lyrics "you can't stop me lovin' myself" from BTS' *Idol* from *Love Yourself: Answer*, released in 2018, that sent me head first into the technicoloured world of being an ARMY. BTS are a seven-member K-pop group from Seoul, South Korea, and their fans are called ARMY, of which I became one the instant the YouTube video began to play.

For me, the Love Yourself era was profound, even though I came in on the tail end, right before the release of *Map of the Soul: Persona* in 2019. As a creative, I'm constantly inspired by the trilogy of albums – *Her*, *Tear* and *Answer* – and as a sociologist I'm constantly drawn to observing how others, both ARMY and the general public, respond to that era in particular.

Not only was *Love Yourself* a series of albums, it was and remains a global message, one which BTS were invited to the United Nations General Assembly in September 2018 to share. Further to the message of 'love yourself' is the addition of 'speak yourself' which BTS presented at the United Nations as a vital step in the self-love journey; one which they practice themselves.

For me, this era and message epitomises BTS and their ability to create art and social movements through being themselves and speaking themselves. This, of course, can only be achieved by the other half of BTS, ARMY, synthesising the group's art, music and messages into action. How each ARMY (and often curious onlookers) interprets and enacts BTS' message of self-love is unique to them. That is the beauty of art after all: it's highly subjective, and over time it becomes bigger than the artist themselves, for it represents all of humankind. This is how a movement is born. Which is what excites me as an ARMY, a creative, a sociologist and a human being.

In August 2020, I started to dream of what it would be like to see ARMY's interpretation of Love Yourself through a variety of written mediums. At Revolutionaries, the book publishing company that I own, we have three imprints: Revolutionaries, providing cross-genre works for the modern-day revolutionary; Bulletproof, a world-first BTS-specific imprint for nonfiction and cross-genre works; and Moonrise, a home for fiction works that inspire, uplift and transport the mind of the modern-day revolutionary. I'm not telling you this to promote my company; rather, I wanted to share my logic for creating this book with you. You see, my interests are varied, and for the sake of urgency, let's just say they're threefold: I am a sociologist, so I want to see interpretations, analyses and understandings of BTS' work in scholarly form (Revolutionaries); I am an ARMY, so I want to see ARMY speaking themselves (Bulletproof), and; I am a creative, so I want to create an outlet for those who aren't as literal with their understandings of BTS and the world around them.

Instead of seeking to produce one book about the Love Yourself era, I sought to produce three: one for each imprint. What I was eager to see was ARMY's creative interpretation of BTS' Love Yourself messaging, music and art. As it turns out, this is the project that had the most drive and energy, and was the biggest risk for me – this is the first book for our imprint Moonrise, and I had to search well outside of my own networks for contributors.

Like our Bulletproof title, *I Am ARMY: It's Time to Begin* (2020), it was important that this book was an anthology. The reason being that I wanted to give a space for many people to respond to the call for submissions, to show many perspectives, and to give opportunities to first time and emerging writers.

The call itself was very broad and can still be found on our website:

> Series Editor Wallea Eaglehawk is calling for submissions of literary works inspired by BTS' Love Yourself trilogy and global messaging. These works may be written in response to the title of *Through the darkness, I will love myself.* Eaglehawk is interested in creative fiction and poetry which explores journeys of self-love both positive, negative and somewhere in-between. Creative works that are contemporary, push boundaries and present new ways of thinking are desired. Show us the darkness, show us the light; show us how self-love can prevail.

Right before the call for submissions went public, I was fortunate enough to speak on a panel of ARMY publishers, which was when I came across

Dream Glow Magazine and its co-editors, Nikola and Padya. I listened to them speak with passion and expertise about poetry and prose, and the more they said, the more my uncertainty about publishing our first fiction book dwindled. *If I could get them to be my co-editors*, I thought, t*his project will be amazing*. Though it was nearing two in the morning for me in Australia, I sent the magazine a message between answering questions on the panel. By the time I went to bed we were co-editors. Excited, maybe a little nervous, with no idea what was to come.

Nikola

It was an honour to be part of the editing process for *Through the darkness, I will love myself* and to work closely with the poets whose words are included in these pages. After selecting ten poets in the first round whose work Wallea, Padya and I all felt was engaging, unique, and promising, I had the sudden realisation that I needed to meet these people. I wanted to talk to them, to better understand them, so that the feedback I gave would fit their goals, their motivations, and their ideas they needed to express. With Wallea's help, I scheduled Zoom calls with all ten poets in one week – an editing extravaganza that was exhausting, but worth every moment. As I talked back-to-back with poets in Spain, India, Hong Kong, Australia, the U.S., and many countries around the world, I was overwhelmed by the poignancy of these diverse writers having the exact same mission: to tell others how they learned to love themselves. This was not an easy journey for anyone. But it was a rewarding journey for all. I got off one set of calls and started crying, simply because I was happy.

When the BTS Love Yourself era began, I was ready and waiting, having happened upon the *Dope* MV in September of 2015 (thank you YouTube deep dives!) in the best chance encounter of my life. Still, I was not prepared for how I was going to feel when Jimin's impossibly beautiful vocals gave us the first taste of the Love Yourself era through *Intro: Serendipity*. I was floored (literally, I laid on the floor for about 30 minutes, unsure how to get up and go forward with my life). The Love Yourself era felt like a revolution, a huge and impossible-to-predict step in BTS' journey, and yet somehow the inevitable one, the one we all needed. The next week, I had the great blessing of being in Seoul for the first time, when the album dropped.

On that work trip to Seoul, I talked to a lot of young people about their writing. I worked with one student who was so anxious, so concerned about criticism – even though I worded my feedback as gently as I could – that he was physically shaking, his forearm jostling the table where we both sat. I thought frequently that week, as BTS sang in my ear about love, hope, and self-confidence, about how much BTS' messages are ones young people need to hear. On that trip, I met a lot of students who were deeply critical of themselves. They told me "I'm not smart" or "I'm a terrible writer" before I said anything, as if cutting me off before I could accuse them. I've seen the same kind of insecurity and self-criticism in many American students, as well.

A year later, I was standing in the Prudential Center in New Jersey, watching Jin sing the words "I'm the one I should love in this world," and I thought back to the beginning of the Love Yourself era. Love is something obvious and universal, yet how are the most obvious, most essential things often those we take for granted, those we don't stop to nurture?

To me, this project *Through the darkness, I will love myself* felt like a concerted effort to nurture self-love, to celebrate it, to talk about, to honour it. I'm very grateful to Wallea for envisioning this project and for inviting me to participate. I went into this project thinking about the students who I'd talked to about their writing – for some, this had been cathartic; for others, their pain was immense and unshakeable. There have been many students I've believed in but watched them never believe in themselves. This has made me appreciate all the more how powerfully BTS reaches people. Of course, it's probably no surprise, although it surprised *me*, that while I went into this project focused on helping others with their writing and their expressions of self-love, who I ended up helping most was me.

During 2020, so many of us lost things that gave us daily happiness, security, comfort through routines, and a sense of self. I needed this project in ways I couldn't have foreseen. I needed to talk to people who loved creative writing, to send emails back and forth with further edits and questions, and to share my enthusiasm with Wallea and Padya who both deeply believe in the power of creative writing to make positive change, both personal and global.

Their faith in their writing has helped build me up. I hope everyone reading this collection has a similar experience. I hope you are uplifted through experiencing the self-love and writing of others.

Padya

2020 was a dismal year in numerous ways, but there were highlights – one of which was being able to start Dream Glow Magazine with Nikola. We wanted a space where we could welcome fans of BTS and let them know that art that was created out of love for pop culture and fandom had a home in serious literary spaces. Our online presence and call for submissions reached far and wide, and we began to encounter other publications and the broader ARMY community, including Wallea at the publishers' panel. Revolutionaries' mission and Wallea's dedication towards wanting ARMY stories to be heard resonated with me, and it was a no-brainer for both Nikola and I: we wanted to join *Through the darkness, I will love myself* as co-editors.

The process was fascinating right from the get-go. We haven't had issue themes for Dream Glow, so reading submissions that followed a very specific brief was a whole new experience. It was incredible to see how many people responded to the call and interpreted it in their own ways. Even though I have more experience with prose, I loved going through the poems as well and understanding the value in hearing these stories. Together, we decided on the most compelling, well-written, and promising pieces and took individual charge of editing and helping these authors polish their work.

To me, BTS' *Love Yourself* series holds a lot of value. It is undoubtedly the era that holds the most number of songs I relate to, from Jin's message of "I'm the one I should love in this world" in *Epiphany* to trying to understand how to identify love if it doesn't have a name, a theme that's found across songs such as *134340* and *Trivia: Love*. In reading these stories, I wanted to feel seen, understood, the way I had when listening to the trilogy of albums for the first time. I wanted the authors to take us through the journey of characters in their lowest – and finding the root of these troubles – and ultimately choose themselves, in the promise of fresh starts and new hope.

Since Dream Glow was still new, this was one of my first experiences working with ARMY writers, and it was a joy. I loved learning about the way different authors interpreted the group's work and message in various ways, I loved the questions that arose for them about writing, about themes, and about the particularities of the em dash. And the best part was I found myself automatically thinking about certain songs in *Love Yourself*, such as *Trivia: Seesaw*, *Best of Me*, and *I'm Fine*, as I went over each piece. The authors had done it – BTS' message was present all around.

I've loved watching these pieces grow from mere outlines to fully flushed narratives that hold depth and feeling. I'm absolutely thrilled for these stories and poems to go out in the world. I hope you enjoy reading them as much as we have loved editing them.

Wallea

This book project started in August 2020 and comes into the world in March 2021. Seven months, just like the number of BTS members. How fitting. At the start of any project, it's all too easy to dream big and attempt to envision the finished product. Of course, this is how I do most of my planning: reverse engineering my dream books and breaking them down into a step-by-step process. However, the end product is never what I thought it would be, and I mean that in the best possible way.

Any good creative endeavour is transformative, so the person I was in August 2020 surely could not have imagined what the person I am in March 2021 can achieve. Nor could I have imagined meeting Nikola and Padya – now I am me to the power of three, at least in this project. Perhaps what I couldn't have predicted or possibly known was that I was soon to be diagnosed with a long-term chronic illness that would ultimately consume me whole. Originally, I created this project to be a form of catharsis for others who had experienced a form of darkness, to be a comfort, a shining light of hope. I created this project for everyone but myself, yet I ended up needing it the most. An experience I see has been shared by my co-editors, too. Once again, this is all very fitting.

I am grateful to Nikola and Padya for their contributions to this project. Nikola, I have learnt so much about poetry from watching you work. Mostly that rhyming isn't a good thing. I'm still in shock. Padya, I enjoyed working alongside you on the short stories; thank you for never being far away when I needed feedback and guidance.

I am also grateful to each of the contributors who signed on to this project, many who had little to no idea who we were: they took a chance on us. Your vulnerability and willingness to learn continued to astound me, and I am so excited to celebrate the launch of this book with you. I think the chance you took definitely paid off, and I hope you feel the same, too!

In regards to my process with the writers, I was humbled each time I was afforded a look into the process of someone I've never met or worked with before. I distinctly remember two occasions, with Katie for *House of Colours* and Catherine for *Hands and Exploding Galaxies*, where I said "Hey, let's push this as far as it can go. Let's get weird. We can always reel it back in afterwards." What happened next truly blew me away: they pushed themselves, they made it weird… it was pure magic. They transformed their stories with each draft and honed their skills, all of their own volition, all from a place of passion and excitement. From my end, it takes nothing to say a single sentence such as "Hey, make it weird," which can easily be interpreted and applied in a multitude of ways. So to watch as a writer takes a small prompt from me and completely transforms their work is overwhelming at best. I am honoured to be a facilitator in this process and the ultimate editor-slash-hype-human on earth for each contributor to this book.

As you might be able to tell, this project is very important to each of us as creatives and as ARMY. To be able to connect with other writers and poets, and to share in a collective experience of the Love Yourself era, while enabling processes to express unique and universal experiences through a Speak Yourself practice, has been incredibly uplifting and empowering.

I hope this is a book you can return to time and again to feel connected, reassured, supported, validated and loved, no matter where you are and what your darkness may look like. If the Love Yourself era has taught us anything, it's that self-love is a work in progress. All we need to do is try, and if that doesn't work, that's okay, there's always tomorrow. The only way through the darkness is straight through the middle on a path that we can walk together, if we so choose. I look forward to walking with you.

From the artist

My involvement with *Through the darkness, I will love myself* began when my friend Nabila shared her poem *Love in Progress* in our group chat. Her poem spoke to me, and a picture was drawn on my mind that I could simply not ignore. I asked her if I could draw something based on my interpretation of her poem, she said yes.

It was supposed to be just for me, something that I could create and get out of my system. It came out as just a thin line pencil drawing. It stayed that way for a few weeks until Nabila asked if she could submit her poem to Wallea Eaglehawk, the editor of this book, along with my illustration. I said I'd be honored.

Wallea reached out to Nabila regarding the artwork and that's when this journey took a new and unexpected direction. I got in touch with Wallea and she asked me to create an illustration for each contribution in this book, as well as the cover. A commission for my artwork for a book is something I've been wishing for forever. I have always loved drawing, but I've never had the courage to take on or search for an opportunity such as this. So even with the chance right in front of me, I almost declined. But when I thought about the stories that I could perhaps connect with, the same way I did with Nabila's, I decided I would love to take part. With that, and with all the doubts I had for my abilities, I accepted the offer.

It was the best decision I could have made, because each story and poem made me reflect on my journey and my sense of self. These stories have a similar effect to what I feel when I listen to BTS' songs. They make me feel seen, make me feel heard, and make me feel less lonely.

To Wallea and all the contributors of this book, thank you for the inspiration and the opportunity to participate, I look forward to seeing your next creations.

Risa Rinadiputri is an architect that works as urban planner and designer, in her down time she goes by the name risathebi to share her art and illustration about self love, the little things in life, and goes by the name Beebo to share her arts and illustration for BTS. Find her on Instagram @risathebi & @beebo_eebob.

lifelong masterpiece

Destiny Harding

cool glaze veiling rough imperfections,
gold streaks over supple whorls,
warmth pinched by questing fingers
to bring subtle curves to life.

this delicate construct of porcelain,
a wavering facade of safety;
cruel normality surrounded by the unknown,
it will shatter before eternity.

perhaps consider
the notion of breaking free–
torn between desires
to fight to revert or to set alight
this bitter reality,
tapping into fresh strength
(or is it merely apathy?)
to let this creation crumble into dust,
to salt the earth holding the seeds of our goal.

perhaps it is only right to call it strength,
to break out into the world
away from a cold-hot embrace–
or so the collectors debate.
the only sensation piercing through,
as blindfolded I remake this creation
in oppressive heat born anew, is
how wasteful, how resourceful,
how much could be easily carried
onto a new path–what I could have been.

an artist's autonomy is doubtful–
a work of clay and bone and heat,
unceasing changes pending,
the final vision yet unknown.

Love in Progress

Nabila Tabita

I feel like I'm lying to her. They say that the key in a relationship is communication, but I am unable to communicate what I'm feeling. I'm afraid if I say the wrong thing, she will leave. So, I try my best to smile.

"I love you!"

I see her smile back, but she knows I don't mean it. We look at each other for a while.

"It's okay to have bad days."

"What am I supposed to do when I have bad days?"

"Why do you want to make them good?"

"I haven't been feeling like myself lately."

"Why is that?"

"They told me.... I'm not the person they used to know."

"But what do you feel?"

"That maybe they're right. I don't like the things I used to like, I don't like..."

I stare at her, mouth agape, not knowing how to finish my sentence.

"You don't like me anymore?"

"I.... just told you I love you, didn't I?"

She shakes her head and moves away from me. She knows I wasn't sincere the first time–why did I think it would work this time? I try to think of something else to say–there is already too much awkwardness between us.

"Maybe we could try something new, that's what people do, they try something new to–"

"Not get bored? Is that what you mean? I'm not enough anymore."

"That's not what I said. Come on, please, what should I do?"

"If we want this to work, we have to stop listening to what people say, and just listen to us. What do you want?"

"I want to love you again, but I don't know how."

"Maybe you should have some time alone so you can miss me? Maybe try some self-care?"

"I did, I bought new clothes, I lit those aromatherapy candles that they say will–"

"They say, they say, they say....Try *real* self-care, for once. I think we should go to therapy."

"That's impossible. What would people think?"

"Did you not hear me or do you pretend not to? Don't listen to people. Listen to me."

"I am."

"No, you're not! You think you are, but you're not. You keep letting people define things for you when the only opinions that should matter to you are ours."

I stand there, not knowing what to do. I have been raised in a certain way by my parents and I'm accustomed to doing things for them at my own expense. They always tell me what I should do. So much, it turns out, that I don't know what I should actually do. I start to cry. Is it possible to not love her every single day? Is this healthy? Is this okay? I feel like I'm losing her.

"It's okay."

I look up, and she's crying with me. Oh god, I didn't want to make her cry.

"Is it going to be like this all the time?"

"I don't know."

"Are we ever going to get better?"

"Maybe? I don't know."

"I'm trying the best I can. Why don't I see any improvements? Why is it still so hard?"

She won't look at me. She swallows and more tears come out.

"Don't stop trying, okay? That's what matters. You can always love me tomorrow. I'll wait."

"You will?"

"Of course. Let's promise each other to be patient."

I can be patient, right? My mind races through all the times I fake my happiness, all the times I force myself to do things I don't want for the sake of my "well-being." Did that produce any progress? Did I feel different after doing them? Did we grow? Did we really? I look at her again, her eyes pleading. We smile, but we know one of us is lying.

"Promise."

I step away from the mirror. I'll try again tomorrow.

Hands and Exploding Galaxies

Catherine Truluck

Once again, I'm returning to the beach. The walkway leading out to the sand is familiar under my feet. I place them on darkened spots in the wood, knowing these areas won't impale me with splinters.

The sky vacuums up the clouds I leave behind as well as the hollow feeling at the base of my stomach. My toes reach the hot sand, but it's pleasant to my chilled skin.

The air is sweet.

Sour.

Free.

I breathe in, exhale. I sink a little bit into the ground before I continue walking toward the waves and the lemonade sun.

On my back is my sleeping bag, which I slide onto the sand a safe distance from the water.

I know how dangerous the waves can get at night, and I really don't want this week to be any more stressful than it may end up being regardless. While I'm happy to return to the ocean, soak in the sunshine, breathe in the familiar scents and scenery, it's not under happy circumstances that I'm here. It never is.

Trying to break out of my thoughts, I wander over to the shore.

I stop right where the sand has been saturated in an attempt to keep the bottoms of my feet relatively dry.

My gaze drifts down and out, following the rhythm of the water before me.

I don't know what prompts me to turn around, but I do. I'm startled, as if someone pinched me on the shoulder.

The beach is always empty when I come, with no remnants of life in sight, be it buildings or people. For the past four years, it's just been me and the sand.

A large sand dune sprawls two hundred feet away from my makeshift bed.

I feel another pinch, this time in my gut.

It twists and pulls.

It's probably better to stay where I am. But something about how the dune stands, wide and imposing, without any other in sight, draws me closer to it instead of farther away.

Maybe it reminds me of myself.

I start to walk, pulling my feet through the sand, almost entranced by the mystery of why it's there, how it formed, who's inside it. As I get closer, I see a penny-size hole poking out of the dune that faces toward the horizon.

I sidle up to it.

"Hello?" I call out in greeting.

The sand is silent.

Then–

"Hello?" I hear a voice echo back. The voice is small, timid.

I don't know what to say for a few moments.

Well, I was the one to start this conversation, might as well try to keep it going.

"Hi, uh, I'm Kiera. Pronouns are she/her. Would you want to talk for a bit?"

"Mei," the voice answers, then pauses. "She/they. Why?"

"I saw you over here and was feeling kinda lonely, so I wanted to know if you wanted to chat," I lie.

"You knew I was here, even in this ugly mound of sand?"

I want to argue with her, tell her it isn't ugly, but I know more than most how being inside the dune for so long can warp your perception of the outside.

When was the last time someone offered her their attention?

"Yep," I answer simply.

I debate if I should divulge more about myself.

What the heck.

"I've been where you are before."

I'm not expecting a derisive snort, but that's what I get in response.

"Sorry, sorry," Mei continues, not sounding all that apologetic.

I calm myself, focus on my breathing, even as my insides are throttled around. She's hurting, and she's been alone. I know how that feels all too well.

"I just... how could you have ever been where I am? You're on the outside, not trapped in here like me. You can't possibly know how it feels."

I center myself.

There have been only a few people I've actually told about my time on the beach. Including – well, including someone I was very close with until recently. But if there's a chance telling Mei could help her realise that escape *is* possible, even if it's difficult and long and unpleasant, then I'm willing to take the risk.

"I was stuck in a dune much like the one you're in now, for twelve years of my life," I say, making sure my voice doesn't tremble. "And I was able to leave."

This time, there's no response.

Another pinch, this time anxiety.

The dark hole, surrounded by sand that sparkles in the late evening sun, stares at me. Unblinking.

I figure Mei has to process what I said, so I return to my sleeping bag.

The sea swallows the sun whole, and I'm swallowed into darkness along with it.

My eyes shut.

A suffocating weight lies on my chest and spreads outward, dragging along my skin. It covers my eyes, fills in my mouth, and threatens to explode from within me.

Then, suddenly, before it does, a beam of light wipes my eyelids clean. It warms my aching back and shoulders, and I stare into a face I recognise.

Lou?

I'm confused why they're here and why they're helping me.

The heat continues to spread and starts to burn.

They place a hand on my chest, right over my heart, and push until I'm gasping for air.

I wake up with a gasp and start to blink, banishing the remnants of my dream from my vision so that all I see is the breezy blue above me.

My sleeping bag is quickly unzipped and discarded.

I stretch on the sand and listen to the cyclical sounds of the beach.

Inhaling, exhaling.

As time ticks by, I feel an almost physical tug from behind me. I sigh.

My guilt won't let me out of this one, will it?

I stand with creaking bones and return to the dune. I weigh the odds of her speaking to me again, after she completely disregarded my first attempt to open up to her.

"Mei?" I try, knowing that if I don't take the first step, neither of us will.

As I stare into the small hole tunneled into the center of the dune, wondering if they can see me even when I can't see them, I notice that the hole is... bigger? The size of a quarter.

"Mei, did you–"

"I'm not going to apologise."

I fall quiet, waiting.

"I'm not going to, but... I didn't know you were like me," she says this in one breath, and I have to lean closer to hear it.

"That's okay," I reply. My forehead nearly bumps against the sand.

They sound young. Mature, but young. An unfortunate paradox I know of too well.

There's a pause.

"Really," I say, "I appreciate your, uh, apology, but I'm just glad we're talking to each other again."

A cloud coughs.

I resist the urge to cough right back.

"Did you really mean it when you said you escaped out of here?"

Her question jumps from the sand, and the wind tosses it into the air. It floats up into the sky. There's a string attached to it. It dangles right in front of me.

Goosebumps grow along my unmoving arms.

The desperation, the hopes held high as the clouds above our heads, poke and prod and pinch at my stomach. It seems all too familiar and yet, I've never been on the outside looking into the dune when this question has been posed.

I was only on the inside. And it took years for me to ask that question.

What if?

It took even longer to realise the potential in it, rather than the hypothetical.

I don't know how to answer. Don't know how to say that, years after leaving, flashes of suffocating darkness would overwhelm me at work and in private.

That the scars on my fingertips from digging for so long are still pink and raw even now.

That, even with someone I trusted more than myself, I could never fully express the all-encompassing isolation I experienced in the dune.

That I could never return here with them, only by my lonesome.

It took a blending of weeks, months, years for me to distance the beach from the nightmare of time I spent here.

Even so, leaving was worth it.

I tug at the string.

"Yeah, I did. It took a lot of time and effort, but I was able to leave. Despite–"

"Do you think I can?" she interjects.

I yank and pull and the question deflates, landing between me and the dune.

"Absolutely. In fact," I reach my hand out to the hole in the sand and tap it, "you've already started."

Mei and I decide to start chipping away at the hole from either side.

They didn't want me to help, but I assured them that I really had nothing better to do in the meantime. *Not* helping them would mean sitting on my sleeping bag and staring at the horizon for days on end before I figure out why I'm even here again. I could sense they wanted the company anyways.

It's not like being with them will make me spiral more than I have in the past days, the past years.

So, as the sun grows bright and hot against my back and my feet nestle into the sand, we dig.

Slowly, carefully.

Grain by grain.

And we talk, too.

"I don't really know anyone," they say, as faint scratching echoes in the background.

It feels like hours since we started digging. Pinkish hues dye the sky as our conversation becomes naturally deeper, moving from awkward "where're ya from"s to, well, where we are now. The looming mystery of why we both ended up in dunes is one that is mutually, and thankfully, cast aside.

A little bit of sand falls away at my fingertips.

"No one at school?" I ask. Mei's a high school sophomore, which I wasn't surprised by.

Her response to telling her I'm 26 was, "Huh, that's old." (I didn't know whether to be ashamed or humoured.)

"Not really. My parents decided to move us to a whole other state. Not that staying where we were would've helped," they scoff.

I'm getting the picture, but, "You don't have any friends from your old school?"

"I don't really fit in with other people–" She cuts herself off and goes quiet.

Some wayward sea salt lands on my lips.

I reach up to wipe it away, but it burns the scars on my fingers.

Although I don't want to, I think of Lou, my recent ex. Think of what they would say when I'd be trying to explain all my inner thoughts. Remember how they would show they were listening to me by talking.

"I didn't have any sort of support system for the longest time," I start.

My nervous hands rub together.

"My mom and her ex-husband divorced when I was younger, and I've never been close with any of my siblings. Nowadays, it's still difficult to interact with my mom, even–"

"Even outside of the dune?"

"Yeah, even after leaving. And while I found some friends while I was still trapped, ultimately I was the one who had to break myself out."

Is this too disheartening for her to hear so early on into her own journey?

"Even now, as I meet people I fit in with and can trust to understand me, there are times where I show bad judgement and get hurt and have to start all over again."

The sand covers my feet as a blanket would. It nudges me, shifting from the front of my ankle to my heel. I turn, listening, and face the ocean. The white crests of waves peek their heads at me from a distance.

"You haven't changed at all," one calls out. The rest snicker, some laughing, some ducking back down into their safe little trenches.

I shiver and slide my hands over my exposed arms, over the dark brown freckles and light brown hairs. It reminds me of someone else's hands, someone else's arms, and I'm quick to stop the motion.

Where am I going with this? I *do* make a lot of bad choices, make a whole lot of mistakes. I question how much I should be advising her, if at all, when I've barely overcome my own struggles.

When I've barely escaped being consumed.

"I... I get that."

"About–?"

"Not about your parents divorcing or siblings or any of that, but trying to fit in. Trying to find *where* to fit in. It seems like wherever I go where I think I can bond with other people because of our similarities, I end up right where I started because of the differences."

She's stopped digging at this point. There's a quiver to her voice I can barely detect, layered under all those grains of sand.

"At school, at home, online; I can't find anyone else that shares my same mess of an identity. It's like, being in this dune isn't any different than how it was like before."

The tide is rising on the shore, a sign that I should head back to my sleeping bag soon.

The dark waves engulf the sand beneath them before pushing away, as if full from an unsatisfying supper.

Night is approaching.

I let the rush of the water in front of us drown out our conversation for a moment before replying.

"I can't speak to your experience," I say, "but, uh, sometimes it only takes one thing in common to make a friendship work."

Like being coworkers at a graphic design job, or liking a certain musical group, or going through the same isolation.

"And even with their differences, the good memories you make between you and that person makes meeting them worth it."

Is it, though? Is it worth the sometimes inevitable breakup?

I finish, "Even when you can't fully relate to every little thing about them."

The sun is disappearing.

Navy blue ink flows overhead.

"I... don't really know about that. But I do know that talking to you right now seems to be worth it," she says, a gentle humour in her words.

That sentence strikes a chord in my memory, and I hear my name in an awfully beautiful pitch. A whisper of *Kiera* tickling the back of my neck. I lean into it, nearly closing my eyes, before I feel the sand crawling up my ankles.

I jerk back and fall on my butt.

The urge to return to my bed as quickly as possible creeps up and down my spine.

I curl my arms around my knees.

Mei, oblivious to my scare, notices the growing darkness through the hole.

"Would you want to stay tonight?" she asks, her voice hopeful. "I mean, just to hang out."

"I'm sorry," I say, meaning it.

I don't know if I should say more. I've been open with her, but this isn't something I tell people.

I'm not too fond of the dark, to put it lightly.

Silence, for a moment, steeps like the indigo dye filling in the sea.

I hope she doesn't ask what I mean. I hope she doesn't ask me to stay. I just want to crawl back to my sleeping bag, sleep my past traumas away, and never deal with the night again.

"The one great thing about not having friends is that you have all this time by yourself. Which, like, duh, but you can learn so much, practice so much with no distractions."

Her answer and her openness catch me off-guard; my anxiety fades into background noise while she talks.

I unfold myself out of a ball, stretching my arms behind me.

"I practiced how to stargaze – how to tell which constellations were which, where planets were in relation to me. I didn't have people around me, but I had the stars above me. Before I was in this dune and even now, I can see them when it gets dark. It probably sounds stupid," she laughs (I mutter my disagreement), "but even though there is a ginormous physical distance between us, I feel so much closer to the stars than I ever have with anyone else, ya know?"

I'm hesitant to look up at the sky, but I do. And as I look up, everything around me disappears.

Mei's voice, and the sky above. The sand, the sea, myself, nothing else exists. Just their voice and the sky.

"The stars are warm and bright and show up each and every night. Haha, poetic."

So where I see the darkness as suffocating, and lonely, Mei finds togetherness in it?

"Anyways, learning about the universe makes me feel so small, but that makes me feel good too, in a weird way. Like, like learning that everyone's not staring at you at lunch because you're just one other person in the cafeteria. And then I found out about supernovas."

At this, her voice gets high and she speeds up.

I hang onto every word and paint across the sky a supernova as she explains it.

"Exploding stars. Stars look so small to us, but when they explode, they can outshine even the galaxy they're in."

Little white dots gleam against the inky blackness. They are delicate, clean. But then, violet purples, cobalt blues splatter across the negative space. The sky is alight with blooming explosions of colour.

"So even though only one incredibly small part of a galaxy explodes, it almost looks like it's exploding itself."

The force of the paint tears the canvas and the colours seep into the cotton sky until the previous piece is unrecognisable.

"And then something entirely new is left in the star's place, in turn making the galaxy new, too."

I remember when I was in the dune, the sun would leak out of the sky and the light filtering in would fizzle out. I couldn't draw anymore without the light. My sketchbook, the only thing anchoring me, would be useless. It was one of the reasons I hated the dark. But Mei, she's different. She has grown with it, grown from it.

Maybe I can learn to like stars in the same way I learned to like the sand.

"Ahh, sorry to go on for so long. I don't really like my parents, but they did get me a telescope a few years back, and it's been my prized possession ever since."

I find myself planted back on the beach, my back to Mei and her dune. My arms are sore but I feel lighter than before.

"Oh no, don't apologise. Thanks. Really."

Wait–

"Telescope?"

"Yeah, it's with me in here."

I hear their nails clink on the metal and assume they're holding it up.

"It's one of the only things getting me through living in this gross mass of sand. The hole is just big enough to use it with."

"You could use that!" I exclaim. "Use it to dig more of the hole!"

"What?"

"When I was trapped in there, I dug with the pencil I drew with. I still had to work carefully at it, but digging went a lot faster when I used it."

A harsh scraping sound resonates from inside the dune.

We laugh in delight as more sand falls away.

The breeze is stagnant.

I breathe out and look into the widened gap.

One of Mei's onyx eyes blinks at me.

My breath catches in my chest. Only one eye fills the hole, but that's more than there was before. When I come back tomorrow, who knows how big it's going to be.

Before I can say anything, Mei's voice, light and bubbly, glides out of the dune.

"This is gonna make stargazing a whole lot easier."

Lou held my hand, placing it near to their chest.

It was a cloudy day on the Charleston waterfront. The bench we were sitting on was long enough to hold us two and our empty picnic basket. I could even prop my sketchbook up on my legs, folded beneath me.

"Kiera, you know I love you, right?"

I nodded, attention drawn to the pineapple fountain as I tried to sketch it out with one hand. It was wild how clear the water looked when the sun wasn't beaming down on it.

"It's because I love you that I need to be honest with you."

That made my focus turn toward them. Suddenly the picnic I'd been invited to didn't seem so spontaneous.

"You haven't... really changed," they said.

The pencil in my hand turned into a wooden stick. Weightless. Nameless.

"Like, sure, we've learned more about each other in the, what, nine months we've been together?"

And moved in together, and met each other's parents, and adopted a cat.

"I'm going to be graduating grad school soon, you know? Finding a job, maybe somewhere else. And you love your job here, you have since we started dating."

And fell in love with each other's names, our smiles, our voices. And talked each other off the edge when there was no one else. And told each other things we couldn't tell anyone else before.

"I just…expected more to develop between us, you know? You're really great, you are, and I still love you, but I don't see you – *us* – going anywhere."

And talked about the beach.

I talked to you about the beach.

"But I talked to you about the beach?" I mustered, somehow.

"Oh yeah, the beach," they said, mulling it over. "I forgot about the beach."

They talked, but I couldn't hear anything. Sand dribbled out of their mouth, muffling their words. It covered their lap, our intertwined hands. It clogged our picnic basket, smudged my drawing, overfilled the fountain before us.

The smell of pineapple, sweet and sour, drowned out the breeze, salty and cold.

I didn't move, didn't want to. I couldn't.

Could I?

I remembered the beach, somewhere the park was quickly morphing into.

I can go there, I thought.

The sand flowed out and out until Lou was covered, the park, the ocean, until—

"But knowing you has been worth it," they said, amidst all the wreckage, the sand pouring out of their mouth.

— I was engulfed.

I don't think I can dig much more than I have already.

The early morning sun warms my neck as I stand in the same place I was at yesterday. My feet fill out the footprints I made before, fitting in them perfectly. Dry sand tickles my toes.

I don't know what else I can do. If I try to scratch at the hole for much longer, the whole dune might crumble.

Mei faces me from within. What I can see of her face glows bright, even with the dark circles under her eyes. Well, the one eye I can see.

"Hey, why did you come back to the beach?"

A bad breakup? I think, then disregard my immediate response.

The breakup itself wasn't the reason I returned, was it?

I dreamed of the breakup last night, after I left Mei to their stargazing. I dreamed of other things, too, like Lou's radiant smile in the morning, their lingering touch on the back of my arm, the wrinkles on their forehead when they were focusing too hard on an assignment. About how, as I grew to know them, they'd laugh a little louder when it was just us, sigh a little deeper when they were distressed, and hug a little harder after a long day.

After I woke up, I started crying, because I remembered all those little things about them, and how they would never know those feelings with me, because I hadn't changed. I was just as distanced with them when we broke up as I was the night I met them; at least, that was what they saw.

So I sat and stared at the ocean for a while with tears drying on my cheeks. The waves rolled up and right back down, foaming at the mouth before silently slinking off again. The ocean was something that would never change. Like me, I guess.

"Kiera?" Mei's voice rings out, clearer today than before.

So why do I come back–*why did I come back?*

The pressure in my chest that appeared on the first night I got here weighs down my lungs.

What comes next? Who can I trust? What was the point of spending all that time with Lou if this was the outcome? If this is always *the outcome?*

I feel like I'm sinking, like my whole body is going to slip down into the sand and never get out.

Did I come back to relive this hurting, the pain I spent so long trying to avoid? Because, since I haven't changed, maybe I deserve it?

If I can't be loved, don't I deserve to hate myself?

I can feel it, the sand, crawling up my ankles like yesterday, encasing my legs – before long, it'll cover my torso, my chest, then fill my mouth and eyes, and I'll be in the dune again.

"Ah!"

I'm startled by an exclamation from the dune, Mei's dune, and I open my eyes.

Sand falls in rivulets from the opening, which is no longer just a hole.

A hand explodes out of the dune, the fingers squirming as if they are independent creatures waking to the harsh sunlight.

"Oh my – oh my gosh!" I don't know if the voice is mine or Mei's, because our shock, relief, and giddy lightness are the same.

It's no longer morning, but early afternoon. I'm not on the outside, I'm inside the dune, my dune. But I've just broken out.

The waves' chatter merges with my heartbeat until I can't hear it anymore. The sunshine blends into the yellow of the sand and the white of its reflection on the water. It's all one canvas, a canvas that's torn in a way I remember.

Mei's hand is mine; I bring it back in and our face is exposed to the sun. It's bright, too bright. The sunlight burns our bloodshot eyes, the salty breeze stings our chapped lips, the coarse sand around our arm grates at our skin.

But it's all so exhilarating and new and nothing in the world has felt better.

"You… you did it," I breathe, stumbling back into myself, outside the dune, looking at Mei like I would a mirror.

"I'm not out yet," she chuckles, but I can see the proud blush rising on her face.

The hole's big enough to frame her head. From the size of a shell to this, it's miraculous.

"I guess I just needed someone to talk to and help me out with it. A, uh, um…."

"A friend," I confirm.

The warmth of her smile tells me that she's going to make so many others.

It also tells me something I was missing about myself.

"And even though I haven't left yet, I know what to do now," they continue.

What happened – Mei's hand exploding from the dune – was a supernova.

A small explosion that changes the structure of everything at large.

Mei's made of supernovas.

And so am I.

The stars I'm composed of may be small. They may take years to gather enough force to explode. But they're there.

Pinching at my skin until I bruise beautiful violets and blues. Painting the canvas until it's in shreds, entirely new compared to what it was before.

Leading me back off the beach and showing me how to keep trying.

"Listen, Mei, I have to go."

The celebration pauses. I turn to go gather up my sleeping bag. I'm sure we'll meet again, somewhere other than here. From here on out, though, she'll have to leave the dune with her own strength.

Other people can only help so much.

"Wait, Kiera. I really do wanna know. Why did you come back here?"

As I turn my head from Mei's gaze to look out onto the sparkling sea, a mound of sand catches my eyes from far away. A mound of sand that once stood as a wide, imposing dune.

Somewhere in that mound of sand is a me-shaped hole.

"To leave again."

That Ray of Light

Aparna Zoya

What do you call it, when you have everything and still
nothing?
The last few notes in the purse that crack,
the magic pillbox that stays empty while resounding
question marks hang as a threat.

Sitting here in a too-small bed,
I let my tears fall.

I sit silently with the broken stories
of two women in between their pages,
their lives were stolen away,
their written words in winds like unhaltered horses
of thought.
Anne Frank and Sylvia Plath watch me
with their unjudging eyes from book covers.

Sometimes my mind feels like winter.
While I may rain on you, or snow,
or fade away like a rainbow,
smile like a ray of sunshine, there is always
raging hot fire in the pits of my eyes
turning all into ashes.
Venom drips in my words
and I try hard to hide my fangs.
Yet fragility covers me
and nobody can tell yet and maybe that's what's worse,
for the fire can flame high, but the blame never fails to
fall on me.

I was a puzzle of jagged edges looking for a place to fit in:
a broken mind with a bright brain,
clenching heart and kind eyes.

Like an addiction, an obsession–
too strung up to let go–I held on
to the wrong people, and even webs of words,
praying dearly for the ink to never run out just to feel alive,
before the thread inevitably snapped and I was lost again.

Words have that spectacular power
when woven into the right pattern–they create magic.
Magic to quiet the whispers that live inside of my head–
Oh! What will I do when the words run out and life returns?
I will go on trying despite that voice,
reading, about how stronger women fought against
their demons.

But something changed in the music that day,
like sunshine falling through a cracked roof,
I felt hope surge in me.
I may slip and fall in this night, but
with the stuttering breaks of my breath, I find myself
catching up
to the rhythm the music beats string together like we
are one:

"When the clouds pass and the sun shines,
I let words hold the weight of me.
If thoughts had weight, mine would be as heavy as
rain clouds
and they will shower you, wet until you, too, drop."

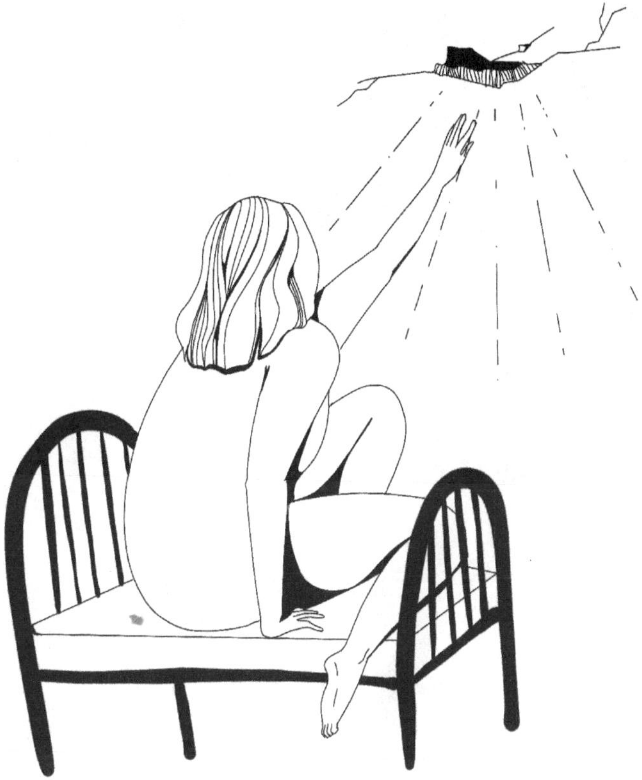

Sixteen

Aru

I'm sixteen and no one will take me seriously.
Sometimes I wanna speak,
I wanna shout, scream,
but deep down I can't bear to see
Me, not being taken seriously.
I feel invisible, ignored and unseen,
I don't wanna be sixteen, I don't wanna be me.

Then I close my eyes, and to my surprise
I don't agonise, don't disguise, instead I realise–
I can speak.

Not very loud–a whisper–
but I'm slowly starting to take myself seriously
and sometimes I do wanna be sixteen, I do wanna be me.
Now I speak,
because I'm sixteen and I take myself seriously.

Twentysomethings

Fatima Ahmad

These kids, these twentysomethings, they come to you and they say I'm broken. Help me. Fix me.

The afternoon is hot. Very hot. The kind of hot that makes flowers wilt and flies rejoice. The kind that would suck away your soul drop by drop of you stayed in it too long.

Sunlight filters through the trees and shimmers on the concrete.

The world seems to be napping languidly like a cat in the sun. Even the birds are quiet, as if they were too tired to sing. The bustling campus is still and almost completely silent. The coffee shops, usually full of chattering friends, couples on first dates, and panicking students on deadlines, are shuttered for the season. All except the Jumping Bean, where a bored barista half asleep, plays Candy Crush on his phone.

On the patio, the four of us – Nancy, Nora, Luna and I – sit at our favourite table, under the shade of an umbrella. Our hair is messy and we're in our pyjamas. With no professors to impress or boys to flirt with, we wear flip flops and no makeup. Cups of tea sit on the table in front of us. I'm pretty sure the barista has been low key judging us for ordering it in this weather.

A comfortable silence hangs in the air, the only sound being the buzz of an occasional fly and the tapping of nails on touchscreens. It feels like we are in our own little world and nothing else exists. It reminds me of the opening chapters of Frances Hodgson Burnett's *The Secret Garden.*

"'How queer and quiet it is,'" Mary said, "'It sounds as if there were no one in the bungalow but me and the snake.'"

The clatter of a suitcase being wheeled down the pathway echoes in the distance. Yet another girl is going home.

"Almost everyone's gone," Luna says. Her piercings – eight in each ear – glitter in the sunlight, "Tomorrow we'll be gone too."

Nobody replies.

There's nothing to say.

It's all so anticlimactic – four years of memories; laughter and tears, parties and presentations, frantic all-nighters, cosy movie marathons, heartfelt rooftop conversations – all of it has come down to one last cup of tea.

Unreasonably, I find myself wishing it would never end.

That we could freeze the moment and stay like this for ever and ever and ever.

But all things – good or otherwise – must come to an end. We walk back to our dorm with linked arms. Everything's already packed up. We look around the room for the last time. This is where I went from insecure freshman to slightly less insecure senior; where we cried over homework, heartbreak, and *The Notebook*; where we laughed at our professors' personal lives, silly memes, and weird inside jokes; where we celebrated the publication of my first article, Nancy's acceptance to her dream company, and Luna getting an A on a test she hadn't studied for at all. This room, and by extension the campus, feels more like home than my actual home ever did.

There's so much to say and nothing to be said. We sit on the floor and play UNO.

Tomorrow we are officially adults.

We wake up with the sunrise, bright and early. There's no time for sentimentality or drawn out goodbyes. There are boxes everywhere. My dad comes by to help me carry them.

"Congratulations on your graduation," he says and pats me on the head. I don't know whether to be offended or burst out laughing.

Is this it? I don't feel grown up at all. I find myself missing the fairy lights, colourful Post-its and chipped paint of my dorm room walls.

But this is the new normal, I suppose. So I hang up pictures on the freshly painted walls of my new apartment and fill up the empty bookshelves with familiar dog-eared classics. It's not quite home yet but it might just be, someday.

Gradually I settle into a routine. Wake up, eat cereal, take the bus downtown, fetch lattes, make photocopies, daydream about the corner office with the sign "senior editor," watch tv, eat, sleep, repeat. Occasionally, I find myself thinking that this is going to be like every other summer when, at the end of it, I'll say goodbye and good riddance to everything and go back to the world of Shakespeare, Milton, and Austen. But then I look at the piece of paper framed on my wall – the result of four years of blood, sweat, and tears – and am reminded that nothing is ever going to be the same.

The uncertainty of it all frightens me so much it feels suffocating. The future stretches in front of me – unending and unknown. Where will I be in five years? Ten? Will I be happy? Will I find myself? Or will I be playing this seesaw game for all eternity?

It's now been two months into "official adulthood," and I'm beginning to think I've got the hang of it. I am mature and rational and responsible. I've got this.

The phone rings one evening.

I figure it's probably my dad asking when I'm going to come by. I answer the call.

"Your mother wants to get in touch with you. Should I give her your number?"

My heart feels like it's being squeezed. I press my nails into my palms until crescent marks appear.

My mother. Just when I thought it was over, with every memory of her buried safely in the deepest and most unreachable part of my subconscious... she reappears like a sadistic twist in a horror movie.

Why do you deserve anything? You crazy bitch.
Nobody will want you.
Nobody will love you.
What will you do if I don't find you a husband?
You're just Miss Nobody from nowhere.
You're worthless.

Even after so many years, her voice, drenched in sarcasm and false kindness, rings loud and clear inside my head.

You want love?
Aww I loveee you sooo much.
You worthless piece of garbage.

Like a waking nightmare, the words echo and echo.

I want to scream.

I run my nails over my arms and watch intersecting red lines appear.

I trace the oval-shaped scar on my wrist.

"Please! Can you just tell me what I've done wrong?" I'm pulled backwards in time.

Her hands gripped my arms with unforgiving strength, pulling me close enough to smell the stink of her breath. Like a dog with a chew toy, she shook me and twisted me with sadistic glee.

It was pathetic. I, who always thought that people who stay in abusive relationships were weak, let her strike me with my own palm again and again till red marks formed. Not satisfied, she'd then caress my skin with twisted softness.

Breathe in.

Hold for four.

Breathe out.

Repeat.

I travel back to the present.

"No," I say. In the July heat I'm shivering as if I'd been dunked in a pool of ice water. "I don't want you to give her my number."

Thankfully, my voice doesn't shake.

After that I turn off my phone. A strange desperation takes hold of me, and I get in my car and drive.

Coming home is a strange and bitter-sweet feeling. My room had been converted for storage the day I left for college. The air is thick with dust. There are cobwebs in the corners and marks on the walls, the remains of my posters where they were torn off.

Sarah comes home from karate, her cheeks are red from the heat.

"Surprise!" I say.

We hug.

She's almost as tall as me now, my baby sister.

I dump my bag in the guest room. The sheets on the bed are mismatched. The lack of order makes my soul itch.

I pick up a dustpan and broom and get to work.

A diary falls out when I reach up to dust the top shelf of a bookcase. It's pink, covered in flowers and little hearts.

Out of curiosity, I open to a random page and start reading.

25.05.2015

Today was a day. Not a good or bad day. Just a day. We read Sylvia Plath's autobiography in English. I found myself relating to her quite a bit. It's as if a woman from the '50s somehow read the thoughts of a high school girl in the 21st century and wrote them out in a more poetic way then she ever could. Ms Truman finds this 'concerning,' but I am fine. Totally. I think?

The kitchen was locked again but there was a plate of 'food' on the dining table. If you can call mushy rice and a stew that's both over-cooked and undercooked at once 'food'. There was a note too: gone out. You can eat this or starve.

Oh well.

I don't really know what to say anymore. I'm just here, floating in nothingness but tethered to a heavy and painful anchor. If it weren't for Sarah, I'd have gone the same path as Plath and be done with it. But I have to be stronger for Sarah. Even if I'm a mess I'm the only sister she has, and I can't take that away from her.

But I'm so tired. I wish someone could just hear me...

It's dark outside by the time I finish. The pages are damp, and the ink is smudged. I look up and see Sarah standing in the doorway looking sleepy and confused.

"It's late," I say. "Why are you still awake?"

"You're crying?" she asks.

"There's dust in my eyes," I say.

My sister blinks.

"I thought something happened."

She comes in, dragging her blanket behind her. We watch two episodes of *Crash Landing On You*. The next day, I drive back to my apartment. There is no comfort to be had at the place I called home. I take the diary with me.

A week later, I turn on my phone. There are 15 missed calls.

It's Nancy.

I call her back.

She sounds annoyed.

"I've been trying to reach you for a week! Where were you?" she gripes. "Everything's ok, right?" she adds in a kinder voice.

I want to tell her it's not. Nothing is fine. I am drowning. But I don't.

"Sorry, I was really busy. It won't happen again. How are you doing?"

She says she's fine. The new job's been keeping her busy. For half an hour we talk about nothing.

"Oh and by the way," she says, "Nora broke up with her boyfriend. Her family didn't approve of him."

The next day I call Nora. She doesn't sound heartbroken. I know better than to believe her.

She talks about how she's having trouble adjusting to living alone. How she's failing at cooking.

We laugh and joke. We reminisce about how she used to scold me for snacking on ice cubes.

After we hang up I cry for a good ten minutes. Is this how it's going to be now? Is this the glamorous adulthood we so looked forward to? Suffering, smiling, and lying about it 'til the end of time. Asking each other how are you and dancing around the answer with evasions and outright falsehoods.

I can't do this anymore.

A few days later, I am called into my boss' office.

"I'm so sorry, but we have to let you go. Budget cuts you know…"

More words come, but it's all a blur. I have no idea how I found my way home that day.

After that, time feels meaningless. The ticking of the clock is like a taunt. Everything is changing but nothing has changed. There are good days and bad days.

On the good days, I go shopping. Cook a healthy meal. Go jogging.

On the bad days I drink too much sweet tea and write. It's not pretty, thoughts pouring out too fast to be contained by a pen, notebooks filling with words, jagged and messy. Like tiny blue ants they march down the page:

When I was a kid my favourite book was *How I Was Adopted.* I am not adopted. That says a lot about my childhood.

I have very vague memories of my early years. Whether that's normal or not I don't dare to ask. I remember moving to Canada. Wearing too many layers and still shivering in the Nova Scotia autumn. I remember gazing wide eyed at the wide aisles and tall shelves of the supermarket as I trailed behind my dad and his shopping cart, fascinated by the sheer amount of things. I remember buying candy to share with all my new friends.

Boy, little 6 year old me was awfully naive.

There were no friends. Only books. Tonnes of books. Arthur, The Berenstain Bears, books about jungles, dinosaurs, space... I devoured them all.

Not that there was much else to do. My mother didn't believe in TV. She didn't believe in social interaction either. Or couches. Growing up, our house never had a couch.

I guess you could say she was eccentric, my mother. She home schooled us because the public schools were "hotbeds of evil." She sewed all our clothes because the ones in stores were "too indecent." She believed that hugging her children was disgusting.

Growing up, I struggled to find an explanation for her increasingly absurd abusive behaviour. From mental illness to childhood trauma to even brain injury. But nothing seemed to fit. But one day while absent-mindedly scrolling through social media I found the answer. There was no complicated explanation. My mother was simply a Karen...

The notebooks turn into a PDF. The word count shows 50,000 words. I find it funny that there's so much to say about my short and unremarkable life.

Not long after, I impulsively send it to a publisher before I can overthink or even rationalise.

But I have no expectations. Absolutely none.

Winter is well underway, and almost everyone's Christmas lights are up when, out of the blue, I get a message from Nora. She's going to be in town to do some shopping.

"Shall we catch up?" she asks.

We meet at a coffee shop. One of those hipster ones. A soft jazz song is playing. Nora is dressed like the second lead in a K-drama. There's a solitaire diamond on her left hand. We hug each other and squeal like teenagers. The barista's probably judging us, but it doesn't matter. She orders a hot chocolate. I order an iced americano with extra ice.

"Your teeth will fall off," she says. I laugh. No matter how much things change, some things will always stay the same.

Nora is glowing. She keeps fiddling with the ring on her finger.

"Miracles happen," she says softly, reverently, as if she can't quite believe it either.

"Miracles happen."

It's snowing when I leave the cafe, wedding invitation tucked into my pocket. I take a deep breath, filling my lungs with cool, crisp oxygen. There's happiness in the air and it's contagious. Whatever's going to happen tomorrow, today is a good day. A day when I'm happy to be alive.

Too wired to sleep or relax, I open my laptop hoping to catch up on some work. A notification pops up.

One new email.

> Dear Ms Day,
>
> On behalf of our literary editors, we are pleased to announce the acceptance of your manuscript *Imperfectly Perfect: Through the darkness, I will love myself.* Your submission is well thought out and tells a story we believe many will be able to relate to. You show great depth, create fantastic imagery, and evoke many complex emotions with your writing.
>
> We congratulate you again on your acceptance.

I have to read it three times before it sinks in.

I want to laugh wildly, dance crazily, scream from the rooftops. I want to grab someone and tell them "Look! Good things do happen."

My breath is quickening.

My heart is racing.

I feel alive.

I feel ok.

I feel fine.

I feel so fine.

I don't know how or why, but I'm travelling back in time again.

There were tiny elephants dancing on my skull.

That seemed to be the only logical explanation. I dealt with migraines on a regular basis. This was not a migraine.

The light was much too bright. It seeped through my eyelids no matter how hard I tried to scrunch them closed.

Where was I? What was going on? One second I was in math class and the next...

"You're in the hospital. You fainted, and your mother brought you in. She just went to get some coffee."

The voice was unfamiliar but gentle.

"Can you open your eyes a little, please?"

I lifted my eyelids the tiniest bit possible.

A hand appeared in front of my face. Then a bright light.

"We're giving you some glucose and you'll be just fine."

Glucose. That would mean a needle.

There was a needle in my arm.

The moment I realized that, everything went fuzzy again.

The next time I opened my eyes, the elephants were gone. She was sitting by the bedside looking supremely put out, a Starbucks cup in her hands.

I kind of found myself missing the elephants.

The voice was speaking again. It was quieter, and I strained my ears to catch what it was saying.

"Stress... any trouble at home? ... skipping meals... quite common... depression ... consider making an appointment with a therapist."

"Oh there's no need for that." Faux sincerity drips from her voice. "These kids, they think they can get attention by being as stupid as they want, then they come to you as twentysomethings, and they say 'I'm broken. Help me. Fix me,'" she mocks.

My mother's verbal darts had always been hit or miss. She wasn't quite the Bond villain she imagined herself to be. This one had been a definite miss. I am not ashamed of talking about mental health. In fact, I'd be more embarrassed to admit that I once twisted my ankle trying to skip class than to say that I'm depressed. But being told every day that you are useless and worthless and *deserve* to be depressed, that was a bullseye. For the past 23 years, that dart had been stuck in my soul.

Not all epiphanies are loud and dramatic. Some happen in a dark room in a studio apartment on a snowy December night. In the glow of the laptop screen I finally face myself.

After a life of hiding behind metaphors and allusion, of self-loathing and self-destructiveness I finally feel kind toward myself.

Perhaps now is as good a time as any to start being honest with myself. To stop being afraid of happiness and healing. To turn my scars into my own personal galaxies. To hold myself with the warmth of a parent and the tenderness of a lover. To forgive myself, heal myself... love myself.

Before I can lose my nerve, I pick up the phone and start dialling.

"Hello, yes I'd like to book an appointment please."

The receptionist calls my name. I get up and walk over to the door. Take a deep breath then step inside. Surprisingly, it looks more like an old fashioned drawing room than a doctor's office. Bookshelves line the walls, and there are colourful plants on the windowsill.

The therapist looks up from her files and smiles at me, warm and professional.

"Have a seat, Rose. Why don't you start off by telling me a little bit about yourself?"

Hey Mum, we are all a little bit broken, but you know what? It's okay.

Lifeboat

Gabrielle S. Punzalan

Part I – *Overboard*

I am on a lifeboat
adrift in a vast ocean,
far from the shore, going with
the flow of what's meant to be.

The boat is tiny and crammed
full of other children who are lost
and tethered by a thin rope
to the ocean liner with adults.

A rusty compass is given
to navigate, but not to steer,
this inflatable vessel that carries us.
The compass points one way,
the bow points another.

We all look to the ocean liner,
buoyant and sturdy and tall,
pulling us along by a leash,
so sure of our destination.
"We are voyaging to your
        collective purpose."

But what is my purpose?
I carry this question
like a weighted anchor
and keep it, like my life jacket,
encumbering myself with
its safety and straps.

“Children, look up at the stars,
but don’t keep your heads in the clouds.”
We look up and cry
when we see that stars are so far away:
the North star is behind us
and Cassiopeia mocks us
for going in this direction.

The darkness we float on
seeps into the vessel.
Cold feet and white knuckles
contrast to
the pools at our ankles.

We fire our flares into the sky.
The adults on the ship see fireworks
and think we are rejoicing.
They don’t know the boat is unstable;
they don’t know the boat is sinking.

The waves rock us around
and threaten to throw us over.
They taught us to stay in the lifeboat
or we’ll sink to our deaths.
So I depend on the boat
and lose trust in myself.

It’s graduation day
and they cut the rope.
They cut all ties that
tethered us to them.

Part II – *Sinking*

The ocean liner disappears into the distance
as they all wave goodbye.
My peers cry out for help,
for someone to save our tiny boat.
    "Who will save us now?"

A lifeboat full of children
is now on its own and
the adults expect the lifeboat
to become an ocean liner.

"They taught me to stay afloat,
    but not how to swim."
"They taught me how to survive,
    but not how to live."

A group of orange life jackets
lost out at sea,
left in darkness, and far,
far from the shore.

The children become adults
and push each other out to make room.
The weakest must go, so
I throw myself overboard.

I am lost and alone
with no one to hear me.
I don't know myself
or what my purpose is.

My head goes underwater

and the waves drown out my cries.
I don't trust myself
to keep swimming.

Will I be forgotten
when I'm lost out at sea
with only my thoughts
and all that I am?

Part III – *Shores*

The currents push and pull me
in no intended direction.
The life jacket I wear
barely holds me above the surface:
a ragdoll trying to tread water.
Frozen limbs and stiff joints
–orange is not the warmest colour.

"Where are the adults? Where is the ocean liner?
    Where are my peers? Where is the lifeboat?"

I am fighting for air.
I am fighting to live.
And through my struggle,
I teach myself how to swim.

The answer I find
to the question I keep
is written in the stars
that show me the way.
I learn on my own:
    "Love never sinks."

A lighthouse
shines through the darkness
and shines upon the rocks:
the beacon reaches out,
like a hand, to me.

I remove the orange burden
from my chest and rise
with the buoyancy of
newfound purpose.

Through the darkness,
I swim towards the light.

Song of the Asklepian

Katie Hulme

Snakes get a bad rap, you know?
Sure, some serpents whisper lies,
but others–
others cling to staffs in the desert;
hope curled around a pole.

Shall I tell you my story?
A smile lingers
as I recount the relief
of wanting once more.

Broken only by a cracked lip,
this expression wears my face.

What a relief to be possessed,
to shed these dead flakes.

I admire my Slytherin kin
who shed their skins so easily
while Joy has to rip mine off.

As She pulls,
I find myself wanting to savor the process of turning this moulting
cage inside-out.
I tighten my grip in rebellion–
let me enjoy these last few minutes of communion.

Possessed, then left empty again–
a scaly shell abandoned by its body
in a resolute knot.

At least I miss it this time.

If I could will my coils to relax,
I might abandon this post
the way you abandoned me
and slither in pursuit.

But no,
shells must simply wait.

Do this in remembrance of me–
as if I had a choice–
you left me wrapped around the assurance
that bodies ~~do~~ will come back.

Stolen Hearts, Stolen Souls

Marinelle Uy

By the time I turned eighteen, I knew that I was half-dead. A moving, soulless husk that went through the motions every day. There wasn't a moment that I didn't know that my blood had turned cold and that there was nothing worth waking up for.

Not even myself.

It's an extreme thing, to know this, to be completely self-aware.

But I also understand how sad this might sound. That I, then a young woman of so much potential, could be so matter-of-fact in proclaiming: "Oh yes, I knew I was dying. There wasn't much that I could do before realising it." But it's a strange little tale, this gradual death. One that many will not believe, though I'll write it down anyway. After all, it's said that writing helps those who wish to make sense of their survival.

☾

For a child of six, home was a small, two-bedroom square house that seemed wedged between other houses of the same shape and size. It didn't have the grandeur of the estates that were everywhere in our city at the time, but it was home. It was random squeals, buzzing radios, and the banging of doors from neighbours who lived too close to one another.

And yet, it was home.

Home had two parents who worked tirelessly to their bones. Earnest and true to making something out of the little things, but unseeing. Oblivious, duty-bound, and unseeing. Plus, I had a baby brother that I had to watch over like a little hawk, even at such a young age.

One afternoon, upon seeing that mom and dad had gone off to do something 'very important,' I felt the childish flames of rebellion take over, so I left my little sibling, squalling and alone in his crib in a fit of rage. It wasn't fair, I thought. Why would they leave us alone like that?

So I found myself huffing and pouting on the floor with crayons and second-hand colouring books that had been passed on by a charitable aunty who thought it would do me good to have things to stimulate my creativity.

There I was, furiously scrubbing away with the purples and reds swirling over faded pages, when the neighbourhood noise that I had been so accustomed to faded, like some strange sucking vacuum had been turned on. Everything became muffled and muted. My hands stilled at the strange sensation in my ears and I looked up. The sun seemed too bright, the air so still that even the leaves from the neighbour's plants did not stir, and the birds I could've sworn were on our rooftops were nowhere to be found.

In the stillness came the soft brush of rubber slippers against uneven concrete. Out in the street, in between the bars of the white, metal fence that surrounded our property, I saw the figures of two people. One man, one woman, dressed casually, hats on their heads, their skin smooth and brown against the sun.

They had stopped at the gate. Our gate. And they were looking at me. How odd it was that even my young, naturally curious eyes could not really describe their appearance.

The woman smiled, but it was the man who spoke first.

"Are your parents at home?" This time, the man smiled.

I blinked, feeling rather out of sorts.

"No," I said.

I know that I had said no, as any obstinate child would, and I had said so several times that very afternoon.

I could neither move, nor speak anymore.

Somehow, the couple opened that gate, even though it had been locked.

They told me that where they were from, there were better colouring books, that they would play with me, and that if I followed them, everything would be better. They tempted me with something very selfish and simple, something my six-year old self latched onto, and it was that I didn't need to worry about taking care of a baby brother, because I needed someone to take care of me, too.

So, I went.

☾

It would become a regular occurrence. Being taken away like that. From six, to ten, to my adolescence, and on and on.

Each time I was returned to my family.

Each time it would always feel like I had dreamed.

Whenever I was compelled to take one of the couple's hands in mine, to take the walk that somehow felt like I was going through a maze of hazy soup, with the houses and streets mysteriously unmarked, it felt unreal. All of it had led to a mansion, though how it was possible for a grand thing to be standing so untainted in such a neighbourhood at all, I'll never know.

Within the grounds of the property were mostly young people, but some were old, milling about with smiles on their faces as they gathered in groups and circles like some strange utopia. It had been a luxury to stay there, mostly because there was food and toys. More often than not, we were given a black leather book to write in, a page for each person, a place to hold our thoughts and secrets, or so they told us. So the smiles never stopped, for it seemed that this was some kind of fairy-land, where none of us should ever want for anything ever again.

But looking back, it was only the children who smiled with their eyes, while the elderly sat back, their shoulders slumped in defeat; I wasn't sure why.

The route back home remained the same as I expected: from that mansion, to the maze-like streets, and to our gate. Then I would blink, and the next thing I knew, I'd be in my room. I would shudder and cry, torn between remembering and not remembering, certain that something had happened. That something was gone.

☾

This was how the gradual death began.

It might be said that it began in earnest when I was six, a child with my own needs and wants, and yet I would be left alone to fulfill a responsibility that should've been given to people who had more control. Older and less likely to fall.

So fall I did. It was a combination of circumstance, absent-minded upbringing, and the danger of outsiders willing to take me and give fleeting fantasies in return. Perhaps, looking back, they gave me the illusion of love my parents nor I could give myself; in return I gladly obliged.

From that point on, the pieces fell like dominoes.

At ten, my passion for sketching, colours, and paint reached its last peak. My relatives found it charming, and my parents would praise it, though not without dashing it away with practical advice: "No one in these parts has ever gone after their fancy. Real work comes first before anything."

So I set it aside to do well in school, to learn my sums and other practical skills.

There would be no room for self-indulgent dreams.

At thirteen, I found that I was good at school and that I spoke well. People listened to my ideas. Perhaps there was an uncertainty in my step, a discomfort with my shabby clothing, and a frustration with scars and pimples, but even so, I reached and pushed to be heard at school, thinking that maybe, if I can show them all, do it all, then it would be enough. Enough to feel loved; enough to love myself.

But all I had was more to give and even more people to please, though they didn't have a clue when to look to me for anything else other than giving and helping. Because I was ever so young, and oh so reliable.

Naive.

Malleable.

At sixteen, I thought that it was rather romantic to date, to be noticed by someone my age. So I gave a lot more. I thought about gifts, and kept track of time, and every night in girlish delight I'd wait for messages on the phone that always came late. But never mind that because, of course, even a little had to be enough.

I found myself giving in to hushed and whispered demands that ended in rumpled clothing, dissatisfaction, and in the end, regret.

Just regret.

If there had been more, I really would've been lost.

☾

There was an old woman next door who I liked to call Grandma, because I had never met mine, and she seemed to like me. She could never remember her own name. So Grandma stuck.

I'd tell her my predicament. She'd babble to me about anything.

One day, as we sat by her front door, she said to me, "I'll be leaving soon.

Very soon. A fine vacation, just for me."

Something about the giddy way that she said it startled me.

Death.

But then Grandma goes, "Well. They'll have everything I've got, and that's all good."

"Who?" I turned to her, confused.

"The Master and the Mistress. All friendly. Sometimes, they'll dress up, sometimes not, but they'll always wear hats. They've got such a fancy house too," Grandma chuckled.

A part of me turned stone cold at that, my fingers clenched in fists with the shock of this old woman speaking of them. The truth was that to think about them, to remember them during the normal days where I wasn't taken, was always difficult. As if the only time I could think of them was when someone else knew. But the chances of that happening were slim.

I did not know what to do or what to think.

Surely, she wouldn't know.

But she did.

So I remembered.

☾

As I blazed through my teens in loneliness, the more a strange, cold feeling would seep into my bones. But every time I was led away from home, I would forget. Forget and come back, each time, emptier than when I had last gone.

Sometimes, during those visits, I'd be allowed to further explore the mansion. But always, always, the little room where they put the black leather book of our secrets was forbidden. In little moments of mischief, I would take note of the fact that the key was always in the Master's jacket pocket.

☾

Before I knew it, I was eighteen. Soon to graduate from high school. The messiness from my adolescence had died down somewhat, and what replaced it was a pale-faced and self-conscious figure, aching to bloom and be rid of the nervous gait that had haunted my younger days. I had worked myself to the highest peaks of anxiety, not knowing what to do with myself or my life. There was a sense of dread. A strange fear that made me want to retreat to that mansion that probably shouldn't exist. Something in my stomach twisted at the thought.

"So, what will you do?" Grandma asked me as we sat next in our usual chairs outside her place.

I swallowed at the question.

So what will I do?

"I don't know," I replied miserably.

Grandma looked at me sadly and smiled. "Well. It's best that you figure it out soon. You can't be like me, just waiting for the time when they'll take me for good."

I looked at her sharply, not quite understanding, but still afraid of what she might mean. "Stop saying that."

Another infuriating smile.

"Oh, but they will. They promised me, you see. I've nothing else to live for. I'm old. My children are all grown, and they haven't seen me in years. There's nothing here, and there's no one."

Something in me must've snapped at that.

"You have me."

"Have I now? I've always thought that if I'd gone then, you would've joined me. They like you, you know."

My eyes stung, and I turned away for a bit as I listened to this old woman confess that there was nothing in this world that was worth staying for. Not even me. Not her cosy little house. Not even the warm bread buns that she liked to eat every morning. The little pleasures. My train of thought seemed to have poked on something in my heart, in my mind.

Perhaps that sense of being poked within came because this cranky old woman – not bound to me by blood or by oath, who listened to my pathetic stories without blinking or judgment, who could only tell me of her grief when all words failed to comfort – had been the only one who ever bothered to ask me if I was alright.

Perhaps.

They like you, you know. They like you, you know. The grief then turned into a strange combination of anger and fear that couldn't be kept hidden. And the tears fell. *They like you. They like you. No. No, they will not.*

I turned to Grandma and asked, "When will they come?"

She looks at my tears and mistakes them for me mourning her inevitable departure. "Tomorrow."

☾

I waited with Grandma the next day. School was momentarily forgotten. I held her hand as we sat outside her gate in the shabby plastic chairs that we've been using all this time, pressed closely together.

When the air cooled and stilled once again, I looked up to find that they had arrived.

"Well," said the Mistress, "will it be the two of you then?"

Not quite meeting her gaze, I said yes.

The couple smiled, and the overwhelming urge to vomit washed over me, though I managed to swallow and follow them, my hand intertwined with Grandma's.

When we arrived at the mansion, many of the usual faces were there. My eyes went through them all, knowing that I didn't really remember any of their names, and that whatever this place was, it would make sure that we wouldn't really remember if we left again.

Here, nothing mattered.

Even when some things should.

Grandma had been taken indoors, much to my dismay. But I couldn't make a fuss over it. I just needed to be patient.

As usual, everyone did as they pleased.

When the time came to write in the little black book, I wrote slowly, trying to consider what I ought to do next. In my pockets, I had hidden a little bottle of minty mouth spray, a lighter, and a little carving knife that my brother owned. I had nothing else.

Perhaps I ought to have burned the book right there and then.

But Grandma was inside.

And so I must have both.

The book.

Grandma.

And whatever it was that they kept in there.

I looked up briefly and saw that no one was really paying attention.

I pretended to casually walk about the grass lawn and towards the little hill that overlooked them all.

Before anyone could stop me, I crammed the pen inside my jacket, fumbled for my lighter, and held it over the open pages.

No one was looking at me still.

My heart pounded.

It pushed ever so frantically against my chest.

I found the Master laughing and playing with some of the children and called out, making sure that all would hear me.

"Master!"

Silence fell.

All eyes were on me, and I could sense their confusion as they looked at the book in my hands.

The couple's eyes had nothing but anger.

Good.

"Give it back," the Master growled. The laughter in his face was gone, replaced by a look of murder.

"No," I looked him in the eyes coldly, "You'll take me to where Grandma is, and you will open the room where you keep this book for all of us."

"Or what?" He sneered.

"I'll burn it."

My threat seemed to do the trick, though I knew it wouldn't last for long.

The strange couple led me inside, to that strange room that I had never cared to enter.

That was, until now.

I didn't know for sure how many people were following us, but all I knew is that this room was something that none of us were meant to see.

Grandma was seated at the very end of what looked like a storage room, her eyes wide and unseeing as she frantically wrote on what seemed to be black sheets of paper. Behind her were shelves of glass jars, filled with sheets of the same colour.

They glowed and whispered, as if calling for something.

Someone.

I turned to the couple now.

"What's in them?"

The Mistress smiled.

"Souls. Hearts. Everything that you are, dear."

I clutched the book tightly and held the lighter closer to its pages.

The people behind me were starting to call to one another in panic.

Some were pushing one another out.

To run.

To hide.

Anything that would rid them of this place, as if the sight of the jars had awakened them from some kind of spell.

I turned to the couple standing ahead of me, blocking the way to Grandma.

"Free her, or your book burns."

The Master shook his head.

"My dear child. She doesn't need to be freed. She belongs here now."

"Her soul isn't yours. Her heart isn't yours!" I bit back, panic rising within me every second that I couldn't get her out of there.

The Mistress shook her head, "But whose is it?"

"It's hers. So give it back. Give it all back."

"Just give it up," the Master whispered.

Give it up. Give it up. His voice echoed.

"My dear," said the woman, her eyes filled with what seemed to be pity, "the world would have no need of things that are too hateful or broken. You could never give love, nor have any real love given back to you. Why bother going back to a life that has not been kind? Think of your brother, your family, have they ever thought of you?"

I nearly dropped the book upon hearing that. The words threatened to sink within me, filling every inch of my body with the kind of despair that could only be felt by someone consumed by hopelessness.

As my eyes took in the shelves, where the whispering little wisps within the jars were placed, I saw that Grandma's jar was nearly full. So that was their game. For every visit, a piece of our soul is taken and stored. The more visits there are from hapless, miserable people like me, the jar is filled with more and more of those wispy things till there is little left of our souls, and after that, it would be the hearts next. The gradual death that I talked about wasn't just because of real life. The temporal fantasies that they gave wouldn't have been so bad, but they wanted us here forever. Other than the fantasy, they offered nothing else. To give ourselves to this place little by little, we would disappear slowly, but if we were to give up completely, we would be as good as dead.

"You take our souls," I whispered, my heart aching.

They dared to choose for all of us.

They did that while making us feel like nothing in our lives mattered.

That we didn't matter.

They were wrong.

"You don't know that. And you had no right to take them when most of us didn't know what to do with ourselves. You're thieves."

I lit the open book in my hands aflame and triumphantly watched as their faces morphed with terror.

It must not have occurred to them that any of their toys would be ruined.

I flicked the lighter again and again as much as my hands would allow, just so that every inch of it would burn for good.

They rushed towards me, wanting to rescue it, but as I threw the burning book down on the carpeted floor, I took out my knife and the spray and forbade them from coming closer.

Before they could stop me, I sprayed on the book to keep the flames strong, and with adrenaline coursing through my veins, I rushed about the room, hauling the glass jars off the shelves, wreaking havoc, overturning all the containers that my small hands and arms would allow.

"Go, go, go," I shrieked at the contents of the jars, freeing them as I went.

They burst from their prisons, flying straight out to find their owners, their true homes.

I could hear the couple screaming in despair behind me as I finally rushed to Grandma, but I didn't dare look back.

I found her staring at me, having snapped out from her feverish pull to the black sheets. "Grandma! Grandma!" I sobbed as I reached for her hands.

"Child, what have you done?" she said as she clung to me, looking around the room with fear in her eyes.

"I'm sorry," I cried.

"No, I'm sorry."

☾

On the day of my graduation, Grandma was able to attend. She sat right next to my brother as my parents came to the stage. I did better than I could've hoped. Maybe the world would hate me then, or maybe later when I'd gotten older. But at that moment, I'd done something to smile about. And that was worth my heart and soul being returned to me.

We had escaped with little resistance that day. The flames from the book had jumped to the carpet and ate it whole. The couple seemed to have sacrificed themselves as they rushed over the flames and the broken shards of glass from the jars, to their demise.

When Grandma and I had returned, I had marched straight to my parents, hair askew, riddled with sweat, and announced with finality, that yes, I was doing well in school. And that no, they need not spend a dime for college. I'd ace my way to it.

And so I did.

My brother said that the sight of me that day left no room for negotiation. I told him that there really was none. I've given all that I could. But it was time to give something new, something more, but this time, for myself.

Much later, when the school and family festivities had died down, I sat next to Grandma out on our street as usual.

"So what will you do now?" she asked.

I thought about it this time.

"Get out there, I suppose. Learn. Maybe work a little. But maybe live. Live just a little more."

Piece by piece, I knew that parts of my stolen heart and stolen soul were back. It would take time for them to feel at home again, but having them now was better than not having them at all.

Friends

Padya Paramita & Nikola Champlin

1.
We met the only year we could have – my first year, your last.
You passed by my desk, and you admired the stickers on my laptop.

I found myself being fascinated with the way you talked about your own fandom.
It reminded me of my own pure joy one has for something that keeps you going in daily life.
I decided I wanted to get to know you because you don't just
Coincidentally meet someone who happens to share your enthusiasm for pop culture,
and not want to pick their brain for all oftheir thoughts on different topics.

Your energy was infectious, I wanted to absorb it.

1.
Dendrite-sparking sensation of being alive and interconnected and awake–
I was looking for others who understood this thing, nearly religious, deeply spiritual.

My fandom became a force redefining me,
reflecting love back onto me,
twisting and bubbling with energy, always trying to burst out–
in words, in song, in loud joyful laughter.
I'd been changed by it, but I stood alone, different.

2.
Your favourite band has become our favourite band.
Like an invisible string they loom in the back of our minds no matter what we're doing.
And they sit – a force, they can't be seen, but we can feel their presence.
Throughout our conversations, throughout our friendship.

Trips to the gym, grocery runs at Trader Joes,
coming back to sit on your couch watching endless amounts of content
on your television for hours.

They're there, and we're insatiable.
We listen to the sound of their voice. They take over our conversations.
It's as if things around us stay the same but our friendship continues
to deepen.

2.

I said, sounding casual and sounding you out, "nice stickers."
With stickers plastered over your laptop case—
colourful, pop chic—I thought you might "get it."

You more than "got it." Swapping concert stories: confetti-streaked,
climbing fences, camping on sidewalks, nothing more valuable than
our tickets.
As you, my new nice-stickered friend, explained your fandoms to me,
we wove a brand new day.

3.

We're five years apart in age.
And from the outside, it might not seem like we have a lot in common.

One day we were just regular co-workers, and the next day
we were just showing up in matching Halloween costumes.
It might have been the endless Twitter exchanges that wouldn't make
sense to anyone else,
It might have been the thrill of sneaking away to watch music videos
at work,
But most importantly, it was the fact that we both have the sense of
humour of a 12-year-old.

3.

Would the world say serendipity built our friendship? This wasn't
serendipitous chance at all.
When you and I met, we were poised already on two different precarious
mountains—

miles and miles of words waiting to tumble out, to level the land between us.
Our new world after the landslide (inevitable because of who were before this):
populated with smiling sunflowers, bubbling pink, banana and strawberry milk,
every shining forehead reveal, highlight reels of headbands, and syrupy fan-fiction.

4.

Isn't there a cliched saying that goes, "music is a universal language?"
We come from two very different places – 8,000 miles apart.
We grew up under completely different circumstances.
Just like we learned to love music from an entirely different culture,
we learned to understand where the other came from, how our lives
worked, our likes and dislikes– There are no boundaries anymore.

4.

Whenever I sent my half-sketched poems to someone else for feedback, I felt like I was asking a favour.
For years, teachers, like Founding Fathers, decided systems of value for my writing.
My words were measured by their degrees of approval.

After grad school, I felt like I was unlearning my reliance
on teachers' feedback. Taking a crutch away suddenly, I floundered.
Each poem fretted over, stitched and sewn, tortured nearly–
only leaving me when I thought: perfection.

I read your work when I barely knew you.
It was personal, probing, exposed. What were you thinking?
Didn't you want to protect yourself? I was a near stranger,
but not a total stranger. You'd have to look me in the eyes tomorrow
and know I'd read all this vulnerable writing.
Were you braver than me or was that an easier thing for you to do?

5.
I look up to you so much because you've followed the path of words long before I have.
I want to learn about writing from you – I want to know more about your process,
where your ideas come from, how you bring them from your mind onto paper.
I want your approval in my writing, and I want to read the words you've written.
We help each other speak ourselves.

5.
I remember, of course, the first time I sent you my writing.
Notably, overwhelmingly, it was easy. It felt revolutionary.

6.
Very, very quickly, you became a person I am vulnerable with.
It's very easy to share things with you. You may not be very big on physical affection,
but you're there for me in other ways. I know I can count on you for anything.
Something I've noticed post-pandemic is that whenever I have a crisis
and just need to talk to or someone for comfort, you're the first person
I want to call.
You know me so well, and we are so similar in so many ways,
that I know that somehow you'll always find the right thing to say.

6.
I didn't hesitate for a moment when I learned you were five years younger than me
(we had good role models in our favourite dynamic duo).
But as we excitedly shoved each other around on the street
(before we'd even gone for drinks, we just had a lot of energy)
I wondered if our age difference fed our playful fighting?

I'd always felt like I got along, like a house on
fire, with people younger than me.
Fandom helped me identify this in myself enough to be proud of it.

You and I embraced our differences
and never looked back–battling back and forth on Twitter, "one brain
cell" conversations
indecipherable with literary references, inside jokes, memes, song lyrics;
showing up to work
in group Halloween costumes; sporting matching shirts we referred
to as "the uniform."

7.

There are numerous things I associate with our friendship.
Olive Garden. Dunkin Donuts parking lot, running in the rain.
But I also associate you with words like creativity, resilience, inspiration.
You came like a gust of wind into my life and stirred up a storm
that made me want to push myself, while having a blast.
Everyone hopes to find a friendship that allows them to have deep
conversations at 7 am,
but also one that can bring out their inner child.

I'm so lucky to share "one brain-cell" with you.

7.

We no longer live on the same block, but our shared moments
look the same. We're alarmingly in sync,
reflecting love back onto each other, and I'm grateful every day
for a fandom-forged world that looks like you and me.

Not All Heroes

Lily Low

To the lecturer who was stand-in family and a friend:
the day before your passing
we had a text exchange
I texted you to thank you
for writing me a reference letter for postgraduate studies
for supporting and believing in me for years
for always being ready to help your students
for never telling us you were too busy
for seeing me, from my first day of class to my first day abroad
you replied me with some emojis
to which I replied back the same

You can imagine how shell-shocked I was
when I found out the very next day
it didn't make sense to me
it was orientation day for the course you'd referred me for

I can't recall how I found my way to the shower
I cried and I screamed
I crouched down, hoping I could hide from reality
I plastered on foundation
an ice pack on my puffy eyes
before I headed off to campus
for first-day introductions

I was scrolling through my camera roll when I stumbled across
videos the team and I took of all of us together
you were always the first to stand to clap for our success at
competitions
competitions you not only trained us for, but also funded when

no one believed in us
you didn't know the cameras were rolling, yet you always
had our backs

I wish I could see the worth you saw in me every day
you believed in me, even when I was undecided on
what I should study
believed I was worthy, despite the lack of purpose I felt
sometimes I am reminded to just try, go for it, even if it
ends in rejection
your voice always reminds me that hard work and perseverance
are my strengths
On the days I hate myself, where I lose sight of my
purpose and will
I think back to the strength of your presence, reminding me
of my worth
despite the number of accomplishments or failures

As I sit here staring at my screen
writing these words out to you
it still doesn't feel real
as I compile dedication upon dedication
from students from different walks of life, spanning continents

Recently I saw a photo of
some of the brilliant scholars you've trained
my heart ached, remembering you and your impact

A part of me still thinks about
knocking on your office door
greeting you with a smile
before we sit down to have heart-to-heart talks, like always,
over chai and chapati
you would share your life, your experiences and

many anecdotes,
always reminding me to never lose my integrity to
success or temptation

I'm sorry if I keep crying
I wish I could tell you I succeeded
however, maybe not in the way we both imagined
I'm not sure if I can make your reference for me worthwhile
I wonder if your trust in me was misplaced

People say I'll be fine
I don't know,
but I have run out of words to say
and I lack the energy to explain further

I don't know yet
I don't know when I'll know
I'll figure it out
I hope I'll do you proud

House of Colours

Katie Hulme

I was happy to lock my front door. I turned the deadbolt in relief – my world reduced to a few rooms with a mere half-twist. I wrapped myself in the weighted blanket of confinement and relished the calm.

Should I really be grateful for something so terrible?

In my house, I call the rooms by their colour. They are used to me talking to them by now. *Had it really been over a year?* My feet traced the familiar path to the Brown Room, stopping in front of a small piano, tucked into the corner. I grinned at its weighted keys; feigned mechanical purity somehow made it all the more endearing.

That day – the first one – I sat down at this very spot and drowned myself in muscle memory; I thought, perhaps, my fingers would remember the way out. It had been an ambiguous drop of blood, signaling either imminent loss or absolutely nothing –but fear of the fall had me descending into numbness, and I loathe numbness.

So I picked up a melody that had been on pause for over a decade and attempted to build a bridge backwards so that I could be with her – *be her* – for just a moment... *she* would demand no such thing as explication, and I was aware of a need to confess – that I was jealous of her? That I missed her?

They drew my blood.
Over and over again.
Ambiguity began to fade into a purple bruise in the crevice of my elbow.

I crawled along my path – forged of pebbles the size of eighth notes – borrowing other people's melodies to add each inch.

As long as I stayed sitting on that bench, my plea remained encoded in a musical cypher – a private line of conversation that could not be invaded by the other bodies wandering throughout my house.

I made the mistake once of sending out an aimless cry that wasn't encoded. It fell on listening ears but bypassed others, and the circumvented felt betrayed. I never forgave myself for that.

My kids began to draw sheets of crayon chords – chaotic notes in red, yellow, and purple splashed upon blank pages, devoid of staffs. They presented them to me with beaming faces, itching to hear their colourful creations become stepping stones between their hearts and mine. They crowded my bench. Little fingers added clumsy harmonies – precious moments interrupted my dialogue.

How dare I call them interruptions – aren't more interruptions just what I had craved?

I ran out of melodies before my bridge was finished. I hung my feet off the edge and sipped a glass of whiskey as I surveyed the expanse, still unable to make her out. *At least I am free of hope now.* But the Brown Room pulled me away from my precarious position and sat me down in the corner of its sunken couch. It thrust a black pen into my hand and admonished me to *keep sipping muscle memory.*

I didn't know what to write. Previous iterations of myself lay bound in penned paper, but these days sentences felt like shackles. Screw prose. *Must all thoughts be articulated to completion?* The Brown Room continued to eye me, so I began to trace myself in borrowed words – phrases and images painted in a foreign language that had been my companions of late. I took them and pretended they were mine until I was pretending no longer. When I looked down at the page, I saw myself etched in original words.

I smirked at the Brown Room.

This was equally intoxicating.

I clung to my pen as I began to oscillate between apathy and euphoria – my wayward pendulum protected by dim lighting and terrible handwriting. For a moment, I longed for equilibrium, then realised the absence of harmonic motion would be a terrifying fate – I wanted to sit down with Grief, not live with Her forever.

I refused to stop swinging. Perhaps I was too selfish to mourn someone who never was. Perhaps I didn't care. Perhaps I was secretly happy. Or perhaps I feared being overcome by a brokenness I couldn't articulate... again.

> I was mid-air when giant scissors cut me down. They severed the stitches of my partially open wound and then gouged me a second time.

I was teaching, and had excused myself for a bathroom break. I knew as soon as I saw the blood – I didn't need my arm pricked again to tell me what was happening. I returned to the room, laughably confident that my persona would carry me through. I and my residents were shocked when their unrelated question was met with uncontrollable tears; all pretense of professionalism momentarily shattered as I lay collapsed in equilibrium.

Grief intertwined Her fingers with my left hand and whispered, *let's go home.*

I returned to an empty house that day – the second one. I remember they were gone, but I can't recall where they were (a wedding? a funeral?). I just know I delivered the news by way of an anticlimactic text message. There were no interruptions to distract me. No bodies clinging to me to remind me that I wasn't all mine. We could indulge in a moment of self-pity, tainted by guilt.

I skipped the keys this time and dove straight for bourbon laced with ink, while the Brown Room looked on in compassionate disapproval. I couldn't stand the way it was looking at me, so I escaped to the Grey Room, which was always ready to abandon absolutes. *No judgements here*, it told me before urging me to curl up by the fire. *Let the flames lick your wounds until they bleed no more.*

There's a picture hanging on the wall next to the hearth, a remnant of my pendulum – it's the closest thing I have to a gravestone. I offered up my dried tears as evidence of my respects. *I cried enough today for both of you*, I said, before bowing my head in shame. Grief gave my hand a squeeze and snuggled up next to me on the couch.

Why, at the foot of their grave, was I still mourning a half-built bridge?

I wondered if I crushed them before they were even born – death by a vacuum they could not possibly fill.

I was dangling my feet over the void again, itching to bridge the gap – convinced that if I circumscribed this infinite hole and tightened the noose, it could no longer claim nothingness. Yes, I was confident if I could reach her, I'd no longer be empty.

My eyes had fully adjusted to the dark when they arrived home. My daughter grabbed me by the hand and flung us gleefully upon the floor of the Green Room, where we were assaulted by light from all sides. My son tossed himself about my neck. Wooden train tracks encircled us in a chaotic fence. Interaction, not Introspection, reigned queen here – full body immersion in a lake of play; spectators not permitted.

There was no retreat from the fact that while I was trying to rewind, their lives were catapulting forward.

Is it possible to partake in two disparate timelines?

I realise now, this is why I embraced the deadbolt – it was a pin stopping time so I could catch back up before someone pressed play again, and I would be permanently severed in two.

When the Pandemic came to play, it shut down my office with a snap of its fingers. No matter, work goes on. But I couldn't work downstairs – the Brown Room would berate me whenever my mind wandered, the Grey Room would let me do whatever I wanted, and the Green Room would forbid any semblance of work. Out of necessity, I fled upstairs to the White Room, whose door had barely been cracked since we'd moved in except when guests came into town.

I erected a collapsible picnic table in an empty corner – voila, office.

She was drab, but the sound of her door closing behind me was deliciously sweet. Outside her walls, I belonged to those to whom I wanted to belong – but behind her door, I found myself elated by bare walls. I might not belong to myself, but she – she was MINE. The light in here didn't assault – it beckoned – and it was too bright for guilt.

Ah, so sanctuaries are White, not Green.

It was kind of her to welcome me in after I had ignored her for so long, and this made me ache to make her beautiful. We had no one to consider besides ourselves – which was new. Zoom backgrounds afforded her a privacy my cubicle could never dream of – and the other rooms in my house were a hybrid of mine and my husband's respective desires; visions dampened by compromise, then strengthened and polished to maturity through the exchange of wants and wills.

I took my time lining her shelves – every item *must* mean something; an album whose words had sacrificed themselves on the altar of a mute soul, a book whose thoughts had dared cowards to dream bigger, a child's scribble deemed "art" by a world-renowned gallery, Korean wedding ducks gifted to my husband and I on the day of our marriage, a journal containing the pen strokes of a long-lost version of me... Her shelves amassed symbols; evidence of purpose, design, and beauty – though *whose*, I am not sure.

I delighted at every colour I splashed upon her walls. She was my canvas, devoid of compromise – and encoded, like all safe spaces. I could set out beacons within her confines, and no one would see. My signal would be protected, and my signal could be vibrant.

I worked – but in between I danced... I sang... I wrote... I exercised... I excavated my viola. My children soon wandered in, enthralled by the look on my face. They rushed to bring gifts, welded in neon gel pen, to lay upon her floor in exchange for time within her walls. I found I could straddle the line between honesty and permissiveness and rolled it up into a few more bricks for my bridge – though I might not need them.

I'd been swinging my feet over the void again, keenly aware of Grief sitting on my left, but oblivious to the presence on my right. No, not oblivious – She'd been there and I'd known it – I just wasn't sure those two should be sitting so close together.

What happens if you hold both of their hands at once?

I looked towards that figure in the distance again – I was close enough to make her out now, and I noticed that she was not alone. She was skipping with two companions by her sides – her fingers interwoven, unabashedly, with both. They swung their arms back and forth, content to move, conjoined as they were.

I looked at my right hand. It had been dripping ink while I told Grief to sit still with the grip of my left.

I was uncertain, but I let go of the pen and papers – watched them drop into the void; words for someone else to borrow – and I grabbed Joy's hand and waited.

Between Joy and a vacuum, who survives?

Tired eyes and dry lips

Alejandra Vera

I find comfort in the cold weather,
there's no need to pretend I'm fine
Anxiety crawls into my hollow chest and dances
As I look at myself in the mirror,
tears stream down my face

I WANT TO SCREAM but all I do is stare

If somebody told me
this too shall pass
I wouldn't believe them,
how could they know?

The voices in my head used to get loud at night,
but now,
they keep haunting me through the daylight
"you're living in your head
telling yourself you're doing your best
when you know you're lying"

You won't be saved unless you want to,
and sometimes
we don't really know what we want

Because some days it feels like I'm the problem,
others I can tell
it's my surroundings

And I've learned a lot about being a good person
Words hold power,
actions weigh more than we like to admit

When you look at yourself in the mirror,
do you say nice things?

I pinch my skin between my fingers
and my demons' threats sound like lullabies.

It's all self-sabotage.

Voices in my head make me blind,
telling me I'm running out of time,
wasting my potential,
whatever that means.

Just like the words standing on my tongue,
I can't seem to find a way out
this too shall pass
and I'll be fine

When the comedown arrives
my reflection shows tired eyes and dry lips,
my hands are shaking and my legs are weak
The words coming out of my mouth
try to give me comfort,
sweet like a hug,
warm like my favourite sweater:

You have to start believing that
nothing is too good for you.

Years from now I might have what I want,
I might have so much more,
and I'll laugh at how hard I was on myself
all the time

Like an echo through the darkness

Wallea Eaglehawk

E

    c

        h

            o

            Four letters, one word, pulls me from my trance.

Did someone call my name?

I'm at the table in the dark, tiny specks dance before my vision as if I just rubbed my eyes too hard.

Maybe they're microbes of the universe, cosmic dust,

or perhaps they're parasites, ready to eat me whole.

A memory flickers behind me.

I know I could eat you whole.

I shake my head.

"None of that, please,"

I whisper to myself.

My body aches, dull and sharp, hot and cold. A voice murmurs at the edge of my consciousness, but if I try to listen it disappears. I can barely see anything except the table before me, and no matter how long I wait, my eyes don't adjust to the darkness.

My memory returns, slowly and surely. Like the volume is being turned up and clarity is being restored.

I've been looking for something.

Someone.

Who is it? I can't recall.

Just like the murmuring at the back of my mind, it seems that every time I try to search for them they disappear. But if I stay still, if I stare at this table long enough, I can feel them close by.

I blink,

once,

twice,

three times.
Something is in my hand.
A flower.

Is it you I've been looking for?

My body trembles and fear scratches at my insides.
I want to cry out, but I don't. Fixated on the flower.

"I hate you."
A voice cuts through the darkness, and my heart jumps out of my chest.

Fight or flight mode: activated.

Adrenaline courses through my veins until they press against my skin, fighting to get out.
I'm suddenly stretched too thin as my body warps and transforms into something else and nothing at all. I'm neither fight nor flight, I'm just stuck in between.

"I love you," I reply.
Two can play at this game.

No response.
I turn my attention back to the flower.

If I can just grow another,
I think,
and maybe a few more...
then maybe [redacted]

My brain falters and my sense of self slips.

Then maybe what?
I whisper inside my mind.

No response.
As I survey the table before me and the flower in my hand, as the murmur in the back of my mind grows, I am struck with the realisation that I was trying to grow flowers in the dark.
Struck so hard I tremble and shake uncontrollably for half a minute.
I count backwards while I wait to be restored to my vessel.

29

28

27

26

25

24

23

22

21

20

18

7

3

11

19

2

17

13

15

14

12

10

9

4

7

6

5

3

1.

A question floats towards me as I settle into my seat at the table once more.

But why?

I pick up the scissors that sat close by and maneuver them to the base of the flower. I don't know how to propagate flowers, but I may as well try.

I count the nodes.

One for you,

one for me,

I slide the scissors up the stem,

one for the voice inside my head.

My hands tremble as the voice grows louder, from a murmur into a shout that merges with the voice that cut through the darkness.

"I hate you," it says again.

My heart continues to race as my adrenaline peaks without end. Numbness shoots through my body as my mind contorts in agony.

Here comes another low,
it's happening again,
this sickness knows no end;

fight or flight, Echo.

Three nodes up I make the cut. Desperate for this flower to save me,
S(cut)**A**(cut)**V**(cut)**E**(cut)**M**(cut)**E**.

But I was already gone.

Becoming one with the darkness.

The sap from the stem runs like the dark tar that falls from my mouth. I cut too much, too soon. Now my lungs are full of molasses.

Kill me sweetly.

But still, I need more to stave this low. I must cut and cut again, even if it kills me.

My levels plummet through the floor and my heart breaks through its bone chamber.

140 bpm, but I'm no song.

The flower contorts in my hand; tar runs from my nose and smothers the petals.

Drip,

drip,

drip.

Transformed from peony to black

dahlia

murder.

I look again, and one flower has turned to five.

I cut them cleanly in half.

Severed.

But there's no mystery here.

It was me who killed them. Though they wouldn't have lasted much longer in the darkness anyway.

Without them, I fear no light will find me here.

I peel the raindrops from the sky and paint a posy blue and g–

That's not the sky,

it's just the underside of the roof.

What is the word I'm looking for? I think to myself.

Time goes

tick,

tick,

tick.

"Ceiling."

The word reverberates around me, penetrating the depths of the darkness that my eyes can't quite decipher.

It bounces around the room, growing in volume and expanse as it morphs from monotonous to hellsound to consume me whole.

Why does ceiling sound like falling?

I peel the raindrops from the ~~falling~~ ceiling once more. This time they're just crystallised sugar that seeped from my stomach through the muscle and skin of my abdomen. The ceiling is a sponge of my regrets, and it can't hold much more.

The treacle coating my mouth and pooling in my lungs brings a moment of reprieve, and I'm afforded a moment of clarity. I can see clearly now that the

tar has absorbed into my system and mixes with my blood until it runs black.
Drip,
drip,
drip from my fingertips.
Pricked one-too-many times trying to take thorns off roses.
For the sake of art.
Cocoons covered in spikes hang suspended from thin gallery wire, attached to the plate at the bottom of my wrist. Swinging like pendulums, propelled by the sound of falling that once came from my lips many seconds ago.
Only in chaos can I think clearly.
Perhaps I can find peace when everyone starts screaming.

My mind is back and yet my heart still beats at 140 hurts a minute.
Ceiling sounds like
feeling
and reminds me of
clinging.
But I look to my hands and there's nothing to cling to
because I lost you when I lost myself.
Without you weighing me down like a 5'9" lead balloon, I feel like I'm flying
which is a problem, because
I'm terrified of falling.

I hate to say it,
but
I
miss
you,
and
I
miss
me
more.
I don't think I'm coming back.

I cover my eyes with a posy in each hand as I fall from my chair. All the words I once held back pull me under with eager fingers, clasping at the petals I tried to grow in the dark.

They reach down my throat and pull my lungs out.
So I inhale the sky; a cloud in my chest.
Now my heart ~~break~~ beat is muffled by the cirrus which expels from my lips.
Time slows.
In the break of silence I weep.
Drip.

Drip.

Drip.
Not even my tears can revive the corpses of flowers that lay strewn across the tabletop; another sign that I am not the phoenix I want to be. I am consumed by a fire of hate for myself and all I cannot do.
And a fear of all I might.
I cannot rise from these ashes, not today.

Time bends.
I scream
"Who am I when I have nothing left?"
into the gap between my bed and my sternum.

I connect the dots.

They lead me back to [redacted].
I shake my head.
They lead me back to y[redacted].
Again.
They lead me back to yo[redacted].
Once more.

[redacted] you.

In conversation with my ego.
"A glistening stellium, north node in Sagittarius."

"That's why it's destiny."

c
o
n
n
e
c
t
Our moons in the nodes,
like my lymphs and your shoots.

You want to be a tall tree that
spreads its branches wide
and sets down roots.

I want to be the flower that blooms for you.
d
i
s
c
o
n
n
e
c
t

"I get it now,"

The conversation continues.

"You're just a projection of my ego."

Time ceases to exist.

You

are

me.

and

I

am

you.

I survey the table of experiments before me.
Last year, I grew flowers for you in my secret garden.
This year, I'm buried six feet under.

Using
magic
to
photosynthesise
my
love
for
you.

So you can find me. Because

if

you

can

see me,

if you can love me.

Then I can, too.

Resurrection.

I carve a hole into my chest to free my beating heart.

No

hes

it

ation.

Stab,

rip,

stab,

breaking through the sternum.

It's hard work, but honest.

"I hate you," the voice returns.

"I love you."

I plunge the knife deeper.

"I hate you," the voice grows louder.

I pause and think.

"I hate you, too,"

I whisper, discarding the knife on the table.

The truth I evaded for far too long.

"Do you get it now?"

You move from the back of my mind,

from the corner of the room,

to sit at the table before me.

My heart stops, and my memories flood back.

Only

when I look

at the flowers
can

I

see

you.

That's why I grew them.
So I could see you once more.

"B-b-but they're dead,"
I stammer.
"How can I see you when they're dead?"

I let out a sob; my tears run tracks down my face.
You raise a finger and point straight ahead.
I try my hardest not to look at you, yet I can still see you.
How, I'm not sure.
I follow the line of your finger and let out a gasp.
A flower blooming from my chest.

Realisation.

My head jerks up and we are eye to eye.
You're smiling.

"Echo,"
I nod.

"Echo," you reply.

Altum

Eris Sker

my skin whispers wearily. wilting bones stretch under
wary gazes. stirring, I might see where the sun sinks
the first time and the time after that, and after that.
until I feel the light creep under my skin in a giddy crawl, light
crocheted over stencilled bones, pulling on my stomach–
stones beneath that, and beneath that
a sea call, siren song, shanty.

slip in, steady–
seaweed tangling in my teeth, dip in and drown
or try and try to swim in shadowed sand. if I am a shade,
the burden of my body echoes
(weary, weary, weary)
stored in joints, spooned from caveats and out
into cesspools.

I am departing, sparring with a rage of butterflies, silkmoths,
swarms of grief. welling up, I sprout wings, flying, buzzing,
rising the first time.
melted beeswax on my back, I topple into foam.
alternatively, ceasing to be empty means
rising the time after that.
filling yourself with dynamite. waking up and seeing
height is as frightening as sea-depth.

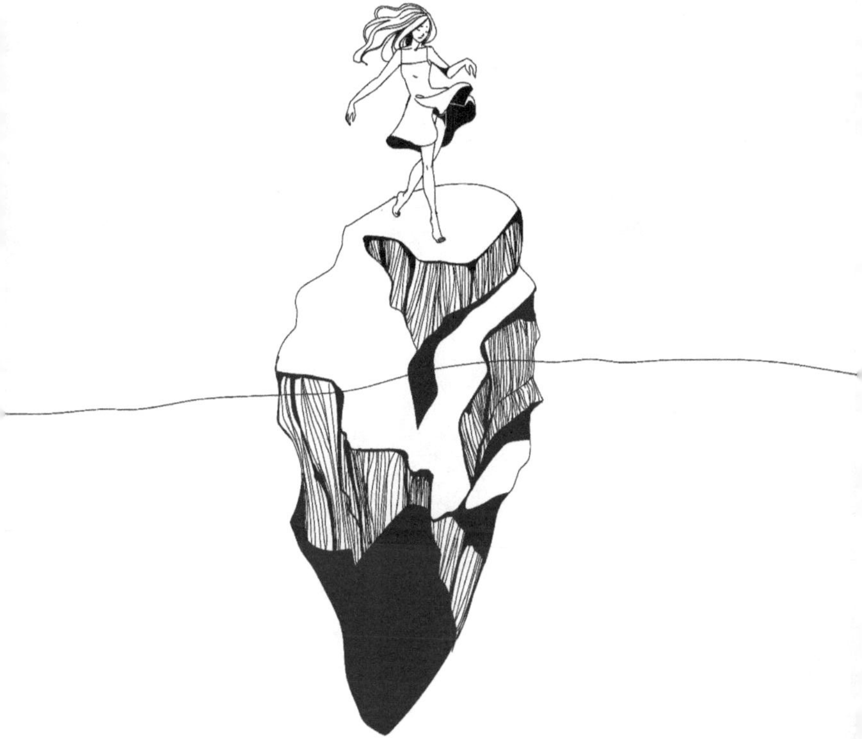

SUNNY + MOON

Ella Fenn

MOON - *Now.*

I walk through the door and glance down the hall towards the bedroom.

"You can't still be in bed?" I call out, walking towards the living room window and glancing at the street. The pavement is bustling with pedestrians.

"Come on, I know you're mad, but you can't stay in bed all day. You already did that three times this week."

A distant thud comes from the bedroom as if she just rolled out of bed. Soft footsteps pad down the hall, and then the bathroom door slams shut.

I let out a resigned sigh. "Already better than yesterday."

SUNNY - *Before.*

I burst into the bathroom, slamming the door shut and locking it behind me.

Enunciate, Cassandra. I raised you better than that. My mother's words echo inside my head as I sob at my reflection.

Sound the words out like I taught you – and take your hair down, what did I tell you about tying your–

I yank hard on my ponytail, my hair tumbling all around my face as sobs wrack through me uncontrollably, my chest rising and falling in fast, panicked gasps.

Footsteps rush down the hall outside, and the doorknob jiggles urgently.

"Babe," his voice is muffled by the door.

Do you want your classmates to think you're stupid? No? Then read it again.

I sob harder and rub at my ears, even though the voice is coming from somewhere else inside me.

The doorknob rattles again, but the voice in my head makes it easy to ignore. I don't deserve his compassion, I don't deserve his patience, and–

Jude bursts through the door, the butter knife he used to force the lock clutched in one fist.

I struggle to catch a breath through the tightness in my chest, sobbing as our eyes meet in the mirror.

What did I tell you, Cassandra, people are always watching you–

Jude raises a hand like he's trying to calm a spooked animal.

"Deep breath and hold," his voice is low and calm, instantly soothing some of my distress.

I try to do as I'm told.

"It's okay, you're okay, just breathe…" He maintains a running commentary, knowing the sound of his voice helps to drown out *hers.*

I brace against the bathroom counter and keep holding his gaze in the mirror as I slowly regain control of my breath, each inhale longer than the last.

"That's it, breathe…" Jude says, nodding encouragingly. "You're safe."

He takes slow steps towards me until I can feel the heat of his body at my back.

"You're safe," he repeats to my reflection.

"I'm safe," I say in one breath.

His hand covers one of mine on the counter, and the weight of it helps ground me further.

"You're calm," he says.

I concentrate on matching my breaths to what I can feel of his own behind me.

"I'm calm," I repeat once my exhales begin to even out.

"And you're okay."

The tear tracks down my face suggest otherwise, but I repeat after Jude anyway.

"I'm okay."

He strokes my arm comfortingly, the sensation pulling me the rest of the way out of my head. The feeling of self-loathing eases, making way for common sense, because, really…

"I'm okay."

MOON – *Now.*

I'm waiting outside the building where she has her upcoming class presentation. She appears in the distance, her shoulders tense and brows furrowed with nerves.

"Remember, they're *just* people," I start reassuring her as soon as she's within earshot. "They're harmless! Well – mostly, anyway. And nobody thinks you're a–" she breezes past me, breath huffing on a little whine. I spin around and follow her, preparing to talk her down as she stops at the wall by the front steps.

She plants her back against the bricks, her bag swinging against her side as her chest expands and stills as she holds her breath. I stop in front of her and count in my head.

...five, six, seven – she slowly releases the breath before repeating the exercise.

I wait patiently, watching closely *just in case...* but the tension eases from her face on the next exhale, and she leans her head back against the wall.

"Hey. You can do this."

Sometimes the affirmation is enough to get her through.

When she speaks next, there is conviction in her tone.

"I can do this."

I step back as she pushes off the wall and heads into the building.

SUNNY – *Before.*

I instantly know something's off just by the look of my house. I slowly trudge up the front stairs, hoping that the alcohol has already knocked my mother out. I shut the screen and front door behind me, but I must not have been quiet enough, because I hear her from the kitchen.

"Where have you been? It's almost 7, and the fridge is empty."

My hand clenches around the bag of groceries I'm holding.

"I had class, and I went to the store after."

My mother is sitting at the head of the table. I glance nervously at the empty bottle of wine and the half-full glass next to her hand.

"Did you stop by the chemist as well?"

I shake my head no.

"Your prescription isn't valid anymore, remember? You have to get it refilled."

She sighs and stands, taking her glass with her as I put the grocery bag on the table. The alcohol on her breath is acrid as she leans past me to look into the bag. She moves to brush a strand of hair back from my face. I try not to flinch.

"You're a good girl, Cassandra," her words slur as she drops a heavy hand on my shoulder.

I gasp and recoil when she squeezes tightly, her thumb digging into the soft spot above my collarbone.

"Don't ever change, okay?" She whispers harshly, desperation sour on her breath. "Never change, Cassandra. Always be good–"

A loud knock at the door cuts her off.

I twist away in a hurry, wrenching myself from her grip without waiting for her to finish.

I leave the groceries where they are and head back down the hall, grateful for whomever had decided to knock on our door.

I check just once that she's not in view before greeting our guest.

I don't recognise him for a minute in the waning daylight, but then my memory kicks in.

"You."

Barricade Guy from last night.

He flicks his hand up in front of him, my driver's licence pinned between his first two fingers like he's about to perform a card trick.

"Guess what you left at the bar."

I huff out a small laugh.

I check behind me once more, reluctant to return to the microwave meal and an evening of walking on eggshells. It only takes me a second to decide that he's the better option, so I snatch my ID from between his fingers and–

"Have you had dinner?" I blurt out.

Fast.

Like ripping off a Band-Aid.

His eyes widen. But just as quickly the surprise in his face fades and is replaced by a thoughtful expression.

"I could eat."

And just like that, I reach for the front door and pull it shut behind me without looking back.

MOON - *Now.*

I'm loitering in the hallway, hastily sidestepping as students start exiting the classroom.

"Sorry," I mutter, quickly avoiding someone else. I hate the way my skin prickles when I bump into people, so I sweep an arm out through the air and motion them all forward, "go ahead, sorry."

She's taking her time packing up her stuff, as usual. I lean against the door frame, watching her with raised eyebrows. I can see the speech cards stacked in her hands.

"I told you you could do it," I say smugly. "I bet you didn't even hear her voice once."

Still staring at the cards, she breathes a small laugh and shakes her head, shuffling them until they're perfectly lined up.

"Now, come on, quit stalling," I continue. "We've still got places to be, remember?"

She sighs heavily and stands up, gathering her things.

"Don't forget your bag," I singsong over my shoulder, heading back into the hallway as she hurriedly reaches for her backpack.

SUNNY - *Before.*

He tips his chin at a spot by my feet.

I grab my bag before rushing to take his outstretched hand.

He weaves our fingers together and plants a kiss just below my knuckles.

Six months together and I still feel the zing all the way to my toes. And when I listen inside me, it's his voice I hear more often than not. He's become good at pulling this worthy feeling out of me. This… "more than" feeling.

More than a crazy lady's daughter. More than a girl with suicide scars.

"That's not even what they are!" I'd said to him when the subject had finally come up.

I'd pulled my hoodie sleeves more securely over my wrists.

"Anyone with a brain would know to slice down the forearm, not across," I'd said matter-of-factly, shaking my head at my younger self.

He'd stopped what he was doing and pinned me with a look I'd never seen before.

"I don't like it when you talk like that. And that's not funny."

His reaction had jarred the humour right out of me, and the memory of it would surface in my mind whenever I thought of joking about self-destruction again.

We head out of the building, my hand clasped in Jude's just as my phone buzzes in my pocket. He pauses a few steps down from me and releases my hand so I can grab it.

The name flashing on the screen makes me wince, but I swipe to take the call.

"You can't call me during school hours, Mother. We talked about this."

"But darling, if you just came by more often… you know how hopeless I am on my own, and you're so good at keeping things in order…"

The sound of her voice doesn't induce panic in me, and my chin lifts with confidence as I reply.

"I'll come by this weekend, same as always. And I know cousin Nancy was there yesterday with groceries and your meds, things are still in order."

"Nancy isn't my daughter, Cassandra," my mother snaps, but then her voice softens. "Honey, I miss you. The house is so quiet without you."

I wince at the familiar spiel as Jude takes my hand and gives it an encouraging squeeze.

"Mother," I say patiently, "I'm at school so I have to go now, but I'll visit on the weekend, okay?"

I hang up before she can say anything else.

Jude's standing a few steps below me and our eyes meet easily.

"You did the right thing," he says.

"I know," I reply with a grimace, "but thanks for saying it anyway." I loop an arm around his elbow and squeeze. "My moon."

MOON – *Now.*

She's heading across the quad with her friend Jane and I immediately sidestep to hide behind the tree next to me.

I used to wonder all the time why she bothers entertaining two-faced people like Jane – acts friendly in front of people, but just as quickly talks bad about them behind their backs. We've both seen it.

"Do not attack unless provoked," she would always reply calmly, belying the fact that Jane's fake personality had always made her uneasy; it sometimes reminded her of her mother.

I cross my arms, watching them stroll farther away. Just as they reach the end of the path, she glances back and looks directly at me as she's saying something.

I flap my hands in a shooing gesture.

"No, no, babe, I'm good here. You go on ahead with *Jane-the-Pain.*"

Her brow furrows slightly, but other than that, her expression gives nothing away as she turns back to Jane.

I keep my distance but tag along behind them.

Seriously, though, what kind of business is so important that it's taken the whole walk to the –

I stop in my tracks as the photography building looms ahead, all pillars and sandstone – the prettiest building on campus aside from the cathedral.

I deflate a little as a barrage of feelings and sensations I've had blocked away washes over me at the sight of the one place I've been avoiding all year. The unbidden memory of bright stage lights flashing into my eyes is so fresh that it makes me wince.

The girls are climbing the front steps, and I throw my hands up, groaning with frustration.

"All right, then. You can have her. For now," I snap at no one.

I boost myself onto one of the building's ledges and settle in to wait.

SUNNY – *Before.*

You're going to stay in that closet until you learn which attire is the most appropriate!

My mother's voice is so vivid that I almost look around to check that she's not really there.

I'm facing the clothes rack, but I see Jude through the mirror as he comes to stand in the closet doorway. He watches me for a moment before leaning against the jamb with his arms crossed.

"Tell me," he says to my reflection.

I'm thinking about my skewed sense of perception and why I couldn't just have wholesome parents who didn't brainwash me to think this way, but what comes out of my mouth is: "Some days it's just so hard to like myself."

Jude's brow furrows with disapproval, but then he steps further into the closet until he's right at my back. The mirror frames our reflection prettily, and I watch as he puts his hands on my shoulders, taking a moment to run his thumbs across my shoulder blades in a soothing caress before slipping both arms around me in a loose back hug.

"And on those days, I'll love you for the both of us," he says softly.

Heat blooms inside me at his declaration. It spreads through me, surrounding me until it burns away every hateful thought in my mind. Until all I can hear is, "and on those days, I'll love you for the both of us."

I'll love you for the both of us.

MOON - *Now.*

"I was beginning to think you weren't going to make it," I call as she approaches and breezes past me.

She glances at the timetable.

"One minute," she mutters.

It's late afternoon – there's hardly anyone around as the train approaches. When it stops, I hang back and motion for her to go first. She's not very good with trains – not since the one time her mother had tried to leave her on one as a kid – but she's improved so much in the past year since–

"You can do this," I say aloud out of habit, one I'm in no hurry to break.

"I can do this," she murmurs at the same time.

She steps into the mostly empty carriage and picks the seat closest to the doors. Her expression is deliberately hard to read as I lower myself into the seat beside her. I know it means she just needs a minute, so I sit back, watching her with my peripherals as she takes deep, measured breaths – breaths I used to have to talk her through.

The train hurtles towards the next stop faster than I'd like, thrusting us forward with a harsh reminder that this journey with each other is inevitably nearing its end, and there is nothing else I can do to stop it. It dampens my mood, and I can see that she's feeling it too, her pensive gaze fixated out the window.

"I'm right here, Sunny."

I don't know which of us I'm trying to reassure more.

I rest my hand on the seat beside hers, our pinkies almost touching. I sigh heavily and glance around the carriage, making eye contact with a little boy on the other end. His legs swing and knock cheerily against his seat as he lifts a hand and waves at me, grinning, blissfully unaware of the sudden despair looming over me. His mother's looking down at him with an indulgent expression and doesn't even look up when I lift my hand and wave back.

SUNNY – *Before.*

He looks up just as I walk through the studio's double doors. I know I'm smiling his favourite smile, because he brings his camera to his eye and snaps a photo.

"Ugh, delete that," I warn, aware of my messy ponytail, tights, and comfy hoodie. *His* hoodie.

I ignore the voice in the back of my head urging me to take my hair down, make my face look slimmer.

He glances at the screen and huffs with disbelief.

"What?" I ask apprehensively, going to him, "Do I have something on my face?"

"No. Actually..." he says, "you're perfect."

I roll my eyes as I accept his kiss hello, but deep down I am heartened once more. His voice echoes louder in my head than the one that had been there before.

MOON – *Now.*

She's already there as I'm walking up. The grass swishes through my soundless steps as I see her drop to her knees.

The marble makes her look small.

My chest is heavy as I get close enough to see over her shoulder. Her phone is in her lap, screen open to our texts. I watch her hold down the button to record a voice message, clenching my jaw at the sight of the last thing I sent to her dated one year ago today.

Be there in 10

I wince against phantom pain. Bright stage lights pierce my eyes and I'm falling from a great height. The ladder clattering to the ground is loud to my ears–

Her harsh inhale snaps me out of the memory threatening to whisk me away. And then she starts to speak.

"Your voicemail is full… so I can't call anymore."

She can barely get the words out. I hate this.

"I… I thought… I thought I saw you today. By the tree."

"You did," I say, even though I know she can't hear me – she hasn't been able to this whole time.

"That hasn't happened in a while, not since the first few months after – and it must be because today marks one year without you."

I feel her heavy sigh right in the pit of my chest. In my *bones*.

I wish I could hold her.

"Dr Martin says it's all part of the process, and I'm not crazy."

"I'm right here, Sunny," I say, the way I've always said it for as long as I've been next to her. She swipes at her face with a hand.

I can't make myself walk around and see her tears, but her voice is thick and shaky when she speaks.

"How strange is it that I'm the one who's here when I'm the one who tried so hard to go."

"Don't say that."

"You found me at my darkest and loved me more than I loved myself, Moon. And I will *never* forget that. And you promised you'd never leave me," her voice hitches, "but it was an accident, and I know it was hard for you to stay, so it's okay that you had to go. You taught me how to be enough for myself, so I know…"

"You can do this," I murmur feebly.

"…I can do this," she says through a sob. "And…"

"You're okay."

"…I'm okay," she whispers through her tears. "I can love me for the both of us and be here without you, Moon. You're not breaking any promises. You can go."

I've been right here every second since my last message – every therapy session, train ride and panic attack – so I know she's telling the truth. She can do this. She's okay.

I made sure of it.

Because this is the only way I'd be able to let her go – the only way I could accept this inevitable moment of having to part ways.

I crouch down behind her, caging her with my knees the way I've done so many times in the past. The wind helps me along as I try to rub a cheek against her hair, breeze brushing the strands against her skin. I try to commit every single part of this moment to memory.

I don't want to forget this. I don't want to forget her.

I duck my head, my mouth by her ear like we're just in another bar and I'm leaning in so she can hear me.

"I love you, Sunny. Forever."

SUNNY – *Now.*

I sit by his grave, phone still in hand.

I'm wearing clothes I picked out without once worrying about what others might say about them.

My heart is grieving, but it isn't racing as it once used to whenever I found myself alone. My arms are uncovered despite the scars, because *he* was never ashamed of them, and somehow, now, I can see them that way, too.

The trees rustle as a light breeze brushes my skin. The afternoon sun warms me like the *best* of his hugs.

I almost balk at the thought of this last task, but I inhale deeply and listen for his voice.

I'm right here. You can do this. You're perfect. I love you.

"I love you, Moon," I say out loud, feeling in that moment the weight of his love. A weight I will always feel even as I'm here to let him go.

"Forever."

And then I lift my thumb from the record button and let the message send.

MOON – *Before.*

The place is packed as I jostle my way towards the bar.

"Hey, hey, hey – careful, man," I warn, inserting an arm between the tiny girl in front of me and the giant about to squash her. I lock my hand on the edge of the counter, turning my arm into a makeshift barricade against the crowd around us.

She looks up at me with wide, grateful eyes.

"Thanks."

"No problem," I reply. "My name's Jude."

She cranes her neck, trying to hear over the noise.

"Moon?"

"No – Jude. Not Moon."

"…June."

I shake my head and yell–

"No, Jude!"

Just as the live band stops playing.

The people closest to us turn to give me weird looks. I cringe with embarrassment, but she just purses her lips, suppressing a laugh. The live band starts another song as she steps back to look me in the face.

"Nice to meet you, Jude-Not-Moon." Her eyes light up as she continues, "I'm Cass." And she hits me with a smile so bright, it's like sunshine.

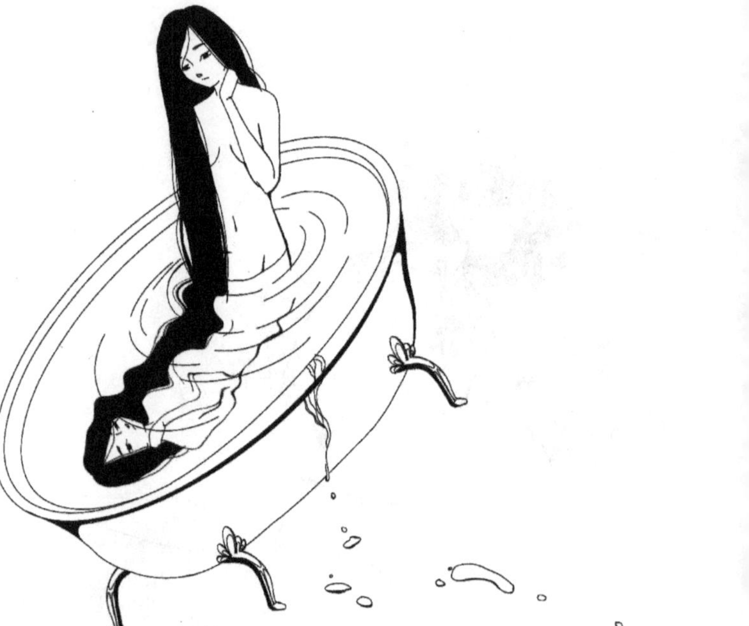

bathtub

Fion Tse

puberty: sleepless nights in the bathtub
curled up, trying to reconcile blood-hot purpling bruises against icy white porcelain,
trying to understand why living seems so much harder than not.

newton said an object at rest stays at rest, and it's not because it cannot grow,
(I want to live, I want to live, I want to live)
it's because it loves rock bottom,
loves the squeaky-clean bright-white all-alone cold.
there is reassurance in knowing there's nowhere to fall;
a break from the unrelenting ruse and rush.

yet still, somehow–something nudges and pushes,
(I want to live, I want to live, I want to live)
sprouting and spreading beyond the lifeless lip of the glacier
(I want to live, I want to live, I want to live).
Icebergs crack under my burning hot fingertips;
red-stained hands scramble and spill, desperate, against tile and grout.

So perhaps it ends like this, with life: that
tumbles from lifeless lips and grasping palms,
testaments to thirteen-year-old blood and bogeymen, but perhaps
no matter how hard I try

I fall back onto cool blank porcelain.

Believe[1]

Marsha Lenin

i was once caught in a lie,
strangled between your poisonous claws.
i bent shamelessly to your will,
and you left me with no antidote.
i was trapped,
i was smothered,
i was neck-deep
in this falsity which once was my sanctuary.
the more i yearned to leave,
the brighter my dreams ignited,
smouldering and scalding,
before collapsing into pitiful embers.
my heart pled for an intervention,
but it was only left with hope.
oh how i smiled sardonically,
when i saw how naïve i was
to envisage that hope was the solution.
hope is futile,
hope is obsolete.
indeed, it took me an eternity to understand that
to be liberated of this purgatory,
your sins,
i had to sever.
your atrocities,
i had to abolish.
i fabricated truths,
so i could breathe.
i uttered lies,
so you didn't see.
hope never could have salvaged the pieces of my ruin,

only i could.
and with that epiphany,
i took myself
out of this hell in which until
then i had lived.
i pushed against burning walls
and faced every demon of
mine
in order to be free at last.
as i had so painfully learned,
hope is akin to fallaciousness.
it is i, who saved myself in
the end.
to be me again,
i had to believe

1
Believe.
The word just rolls off your tongue, doesn't it?
Despite only consisting of two syllables,
it seems to be the hardest thing to ever do.
Believing involves letting go of all your inhibitions.
Believing involves putting yourself before others.
Most importantly, believing involves loving yourself.
Every time you experience something that tests your ability to believe,
know that:
because one believes in oneself,
one doesn't need to receive the validity of someone else.
You are valid, the way you are.

Credits

Moonrise would like to thank everyone at Revolutionaries who worked on *Through the darkness, I will love myself.*

Editor

Wallea Eaglehawk

Copy editor

Anna Shaffer

Production

Oda W. Tolsrød
Paula Pomer
Federica Trogu

Design

Paula Pomer
Wallea Eaglehawk

Marketing

Patritsiya Mitkovska
Federica Trogu
Pamela Gutiérrez
Catherine Truluck
Tyler Lee

Communications

Manilyn Gumapas
Pamela Gutiérrez
Yessenia Herrera

CPSIA information can be obtained
at www.ICGtesting.com
Printed in the USA
FSHW010640090421
80235FS

9 780645 048612